# Silver Burdett
# Mathematics

## Practice Workbook

### Cumulative Practice

### Mixed Review

**Silver Burdett Ginn**
Parsippany, NJ

Atlanta, GA • Deerfield, IL • Irving, TX • Needham, MA • Upland, CA

**Silver Burdett Ginn**

1999 Printing

© 1998 Silver Burdett Ginn Inc. All rights reserved. Printed in the United States of America.
The publisher hereby grants permission to reproduce these pages in part or in whole, for
classroom use only.

ISBN 0-382-37293-X

8 9-B-02 01

# Contents

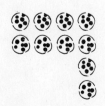

# Contents

Name _____

# Reading and Writing Decimals

Write in words.

**1.** 3.4 _____

**2.** 0.0045 _____

**3.** 5.38 _____

**4.** 27.6 _____

**5.** 0.025 _____

**6.** 200.09 _____

Write the expanded form of each number.

**7.** 0.73 _____

**8.** 0.146 _____

**9.** 0.0065 _____

**10.** 90.0205 _____

Write each decimal in standard form.

**11.** five and two tenths _____

**12.** twenty and two hundredths _____

**13.** 1 tenth more than 6.25 _____

**14.** 1 more than 0.025 _____

## Review and Remember

Add, subtract, multiply, or divide.

| **1.** 3,142<br>+ 6,527 | **2.** 8,457<br>+ 2,431 | **3.** 23,641<br>+ 26,237 | **4.** 9,974<br>− 4,863 | **5.** 20,698<br>−   593 | **6.** 49,574<br>− 28,361 |
|---|---|---|---|---|---|

| **7.** 251<br>×   6 | **8.** 836<br>×   7 | **9.** 152<br>×   3 | **10.** 4)‾160‾ | **11.** 5)‾190‾ | **12.** 7)‾322‾ |
|---|---|---|---|---|---|

Name _____

# Comparing and Ordering
# Whole Numbers and Decimals

Use this number line to answer 1–12.

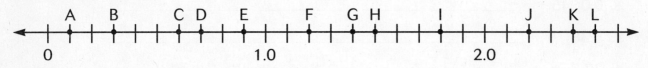

Write the decimal for each point.

| | | | | | |
|---|---|---|---|---|---|
| **1.** A ____ | **2.** D ____ | **3.** G ____ | **4.** J ____ | **5.** F ____ | **6.** K ____ |
| **7.** C ____ | **8.** H ____ | **9.** L ____ | **10.** B ____ | **11.** E ____ | **12.** I ____ |

Compare. Write >, <, or = in each ◯.

| | | |
|---|---|---|
| **13.** 1.5 ◯ 0.98 | **14.** 5.6 ◯ 5.59 | **15.** 3.4 ◯ 3 |
| **16.** 7.09 ◯ 7.9 | **17.** 9.2 ◯ 9.20 | **18.** 6 ◯ 6.003 |
| **19.** 7.12 ◯ 7.012 | **20.** 0.05 ◯ 5 | **21.** 0.007 ◯ 0.017 |
| **22.** 4 ◯ 4.100 | **23.** 3.2 ◯ 3.25 | **24.** 0.161 ◯ 0.16 |

List in order from least to greatest.

**25.** 6.45   6   6.054   6.54   _____

**26.** 0.732   1   0.723   0.7238   _____

**27.** 9.2215   9   9.5   9.022   _____

**28.** 4.43   4.3   4   4.034   _____

## Review and Remember

Add, subtract, multiply, or divide.

| | | | |
|---|---|---|---|
| **1.**    844<br>+ 163 | **2.**    938<br>+ 65 | **3.**    8,715<br>− 8,304 | **4.**    4,093<br>− 2,742 |
| **5.**    602<br>× 8 | **6.**    891<br>× 5 | **7.** 9)477 | **8.** 5)5,432 |

Name _____

# Rounding Whole Numbers and Decimals

Round each number to the place named.

tenths       **1.** 9.976 _____     **2.** 9.45 _____

               **3.** 2.319 _____     **4.** 6.26 _____

hundredths   **5.** 75.046 _____     **6.** 4.167 _____

               **7.** 1.986 _____     **8.** 68.003 _____

thousandths  **9.** 1.2693 _____    **10.** 2.5856 _____

             **11.** 25.0057 _____   **12.** 15.6262 _____

tens        **13.** 292 _____     **14.** 5,852 _____

             **15.** 16,876 _____   **16.** 778 _____

hundreds    **17.** 5,804 _____    **18.** 16,675 _____

             **19.** 9,542 _____   **20.** 1,375 _____

Round each amount to the nearest dollar.

**21.** $53.25 _____        **22.** $499.59 _____

Round 781.4391 to the nearest place named.

**23.** hundreds _____     **24.** hundredths _____

## Review and Remember

Add or subtract.

**1.**   416      **2.**   400     **3.**   619     **4.**   360     **5.** 1,212
   + 211        − 198       + 87       − 42     − 863

**6.** 2,349     **7.** 6,220     **8.** 9,844     **9.** 6,414    **10.**   212
  + 878     + 1,587     − 521     + 566     + 111

                           Use after Grade 6, text page 19.    

# Estimating Sums and Differences

Estimate each sum or difference.

**1.** 0.32
+ 0.91

**2.** $46.39
− 12.98

**3.** 787
− 107

**4.** 615
+ 869

**5.** 73.05
+ 0.08

**6.** 34.3 + 19.69 _____

**7.** 9.2 − 1.8 _____

**8.** 7,655 + 9,012 _____

**9.** 367 − 98 _____

Give an adjusted estimate for each sum.

**10.** 170.85
+ 437.22

**11.** $8.99
+ 2.03

**12.** 4,826
+ 678

**13.** 503
+ 391

**14.** 4,671
+ 2,345

**15.** $125.50 + $31.25 _____

**16.** 508 + 492 _____

Estimate to compare. Write >, <, or = in each ◯.

**17.** 452 + 217 ◯ 510 + 255

**18.** 8.014 − 0.71 ◯ 57.5 − 53.01

Estimate to choose the correct answer.

**19.** 21 + 38 + 43
   **a.** 102
   **b.** 1,020
   **c.** 10,020

**20.** 497.3 − 175.0
   **a.** 3.223
   **b.** 32.230
   **c.** 322.3

## Review and Remember

Write > or < in each ◯.

**1.** 1,260 ◯ 1,620

**2.** 162 ◯ 126

**3.** 0.7 ◯ 7

**4.** 21,000 ◯ 20,999

**5.** 47.9 ◯ 48.1

**6.** 14 ◯ 1.4

**7.** 563,221 ◯ 563,222

**8.** 0.4 ◯ 0.40

**9.** 6,220 ◯ 60,220

**10.** 78,000 ◯ 7,800

**11.** 1.417 ◯ 1.47

**12.** 918 ◯ 981

**13.** 95,947 ◯ 95,937

**14.** 21.12 ◯ 21.012

**15.** 412 ◯ 41.2

Name _____

# Adding and Subtracting Whole Numbers and Decimals

Add. Use mental math, paper and pencil, or a calculator.

**1.** 1,034 + 266 _____     **2.** 375 + 2,175 _____

**3.** 5.13 + 6.92 + 7.45 _____     **4.** 16 + 75 + 53 _____

**5.** 15.3 + 65.3691 _____     **6.** $57.29 + $22.61 _____

**7.** 348,425 + 91,263 _____     **8.** 21 + 118 + 29 + 286 _____

**9.** $270 + $64 + $125 _____     **10.** 1.09 + 3 + 17.4 + 0.6 _____

Compare. Write >, <, or = in each ◯ .

**11.** 0.03 ◯ 0.0228 + 0.0081     **12.** 3,367 + 2,000 ◯ 4,931

**13.** 1,475 + 265 ◯ 4,030     **14.** 1.00 + 0.06 ◯ 2.022

**15.** 4.001 ◯ 0.175 + 3.4     **16.** 327 + 212 ◯ 639

Find each missing number.

**17.** _____ − 65 = 1,590     **18.** 96.7 − _____ = 86.7

**19.** 4,360 − _____ = 175     **20.** 71.5 − 2.5 = _____

**21.** 4,076 − _____ = 3,873     **22.** _____ − 20.09 = 13.5

## Review and Remember

Add. Estimate to check each answer.

**1.**   56,443
   + 91,635

**2.**   385,911
   + 472,898

**3.**   296,438
   + 47,176

**4.**   301,513
   + 185,420

**5.**   9.67
   + 4.35

**6.**   430,655
   + 287,741

**7.**   9,312
   + 187

**8.**   15.65
   + 0.35

# Order of Operations

Solve each equation.

1. $(7 + 2) \div 3 + 4 =$ _____

2. $9 - 2 \times 4 + 1 =$ _____

3. $16 - 9 + 4 =$ _____

4. $6 + 18 \div 6 - 9 =$ _____

5. $4 \times 9 - 27 - 4 =$ _____

6. $16 - 5 \times 3 + 1 =$ _____

7. $27 \div (12 - 9) \times 3 =$ _____

8. $4 \times (50 \div 5) - 3 =$ _____

Complete each equation. Write $+$, $-$, $\times$, or $\div$ in each $\bigcirc$.

9. $7 \bigcirc 2 \bigcirc 3 \bigcirc 4 = 10$

10. $3 \bigcirc 4 \bigcirc 7 \bigcirc 2 = 7$

11. $4 \bigcirc 5 \bigcirc 7 = 2$

12. $(4 \bigcirc 5) \bigcirc 2 \bigcirc 1 = 9$

13. $(6 \bigcirc 4) \bigcirc (3 \bigcirc 8) = 1$

14. $(25 \bigcirc 5) \bigcirc 5 \bigcirc 2 = 4$

Circle the letter of the correct expression and evaluate.

15. Angel brought $7 to the Fun Fair. So did each of her 3 friends. Angel's mother then gave each of the girls $2 more. How much money did the whole group have to spend at the Fun Fair?

    a. $\$7 + \$2 \times 4$    b. $(\$7 \times 4) + (\$2 \times 4)$    c. $\$7 \times \$2 \times 4$    _____

16. Ryan's dad bought 30 tickets for the Fun Fair. He used 2 tickets to buy a juice and then divided the rest among his 4 children. How many tickets did each child receive?

    a. $30 \div 2 \div 4$    b. $30 - 2 \times (2 \times 4)$    c. $(30 - 2) \div 4$    _____

## Review and Remember

Multiply. Check by estimating.

1. $\begin{array}{r} 31 \\ \times\ 5 \\ \hline \end{array}$

2. $\begin{array}{r} 13 \\ \times\ 7 \\ \hline \end{array}$

3. $\begin{array}{r} 82 \\ \times\ 6 \\ \hline \end{array}$

4. $\begin{array}{r} \$3.04 \\ \times\ 9 \\ \hline \end{array}$

5. $\begin{array}{r} 45 \\ \times\ 8 \\ \hline \end{array}$

6. $\begin{array}{r} 50 \\ \times\ 8 \\ \hline \end{array}$

7. $\begin{array}{r} 98 \\ \times\ 9 \\ \hline \end{array}$

8. $\begin{array}{r} \$304 \\ \times\ 9 \\ \hline \end{array}$

# Using Properties of Multiplication

Find each missing product. Name the property you used.

**1.** $(6 \times \underline{\hspace{1cm}}) \times 3 = 6 \times (2 \times 3)$

_____

**2.** $1 \times \underline{\hspace{1cm}} = 4$

_____

**3.** $5 \times \underline{\hspace{1cm}} = 8 \times 5$

_____

**4.** $(9 \times 4) \times 7 = 9 \times (\underline{\hspace{1cm}} \times 7)$

_____

Find each product.

**5.** $6 \times (8 \times 1) = \underline{\hspace{1cm}}$

**6.** $4 \times (4 \times 2) = \underline{\hspace{1cm}}$

**7.** $3 \times (4 \times 2) = \underline{\hspace{1cm}}$

**8.** $7 \times (1 \times 7) = \underline{\hspace{1cm}}$

**9.** $(2 + 4) \times 9 = \underline{\hspace{1cm}}$

**10.** $(3 \times 3) \times 8 = \underline{\hspace{1cm}}$

Find the missing factor. Name the property you used.

**11.** $17 \times \underline{\hspace{1cm}} = 17$

_____

**12.** $6 \times 9 = \underline{\hspace{1cm}} \times 6$

_____

**13.** $(5 \times 4) \times 8 = \underline{\hspace{1cm}} \times (4 \times 8)$

_____

**14.** $\underline{\hspace{1cm}} \times 3 = 3 \times 7$

_____

## Review and Remember

Find each sum or difference.

**1.**
$$334$$
$$697$$
$$+\ 845$$

**2.**
$$784$$
$$231$$
$$+\ 944$$

**3.**
$$411$$
$$538$$
$$+\ 637$$

**4.**
$$582$$
$$-\ 361$$

**5.**
$$498$$
$$-\ 279$$

**6.**
$$8,732$$
$$-\ \ \ 421$$

**7.**
$$5,110$$
$$-\ \ \ 693$$

**8.**
$$7,940$$
$$-\ 3,682$$

**9.**
$$6,473$$
$$+\ 5,821$$

**10.**
$$9,836$$
$$+\ 3,445$$

# Estimating Products

Estimate each product.

**1.**  4.5
       × 3.2

**2.**  29.1
       × 2.7

**3.**  6.81
       × 5.17

**4.** 734.3
       × 46.2

**5.** 1.6 × 3.4 _____

**6.** 14.35 × 16.78 _____

**7.** 2,310 × 391 _____

**8.** 1,737 × 68 _____

Give a range for each product.

**9.** 33 × 59

**10.** 88 × 301

_____

_____

**11.** 786 × 42

**12.** 617 × 356

_____

_____

Estimate. Then choose the exact answer.

**13.** 6.5 × 3.17

  **a.** 0.20605

  **b.** 2.0606

  **c.** 20.605

**14.** 1.46 × 5.7

  **a.** 0.8322

  **b.** 8.322

  **c.** 83.22

**15.** 4.83 × 62.1

  **a.** 29.9943

  **b.** 299.943

  **c.** 2,999.43

**16.** 54.621 × 4.5

  **a.** 2.457945

  **b.** 24.57945

  **c.** 245.7945

# Review and Remember

Use mental math to solve.

**1.** 149
     + 27

**2.** $2.00
     − 0.59

**3.** 98
     + 47

**4.** 129
     − 37

**5.** 60 × 300 _____

**6.** 400 × 3 _____

**7.** 900 × 80 _____

**8.** 70 × 80 _____

**9.** 2,000 × 40 _____

**10.** 500 × 500 _____

# Multiplying Whole Numbers

Use patterns to find each product.

**1.** $10 \times 3$ _____   **2.** $100 \times 3$ _____   **3.** $1{,}000 \times 3$ _____

**4.** $6 \times 90$ _____   **5.** $6 \times 900$ _____   **6.** $6 \times 90{,}000$ _____

**7.** $7 \times 40$ _____   **8.** $70 \times 40$ _____   **9.** $700 \times 400$ _____

Follow the rule to find each missing number.

Rule: Multiply by 50

| | Input | Output |
|---|---|---|
| **10.** | 60 | |
| **11.** | 200 | |
| **12.** | | 45,000 |

Rule: Multiply by 814

| | Input | Output |
|---|---|---|
| **13.** | 37 | |
| **14.** | | 42,328 |
| **15.** | 84 | |

Multiply. Estimate to be sure each product makes sense.

**16.**   830
$\times\ 27$

**17.**   576
$\times\ 63$

**18.**   7,423
$\times\ \ \ 71$

**19.**   8,543
$\times\ \ \ 92$

**20.**   1,657
$\times\ \ \ 89$

## Review and Remember

Add or subtract.

**1.**   586
$+\ 335$

**2.**   2,607
$+\ \ \ 123$

**3.**   1,635
$+\ 1{,}978$

**4.**   8,380
$+\ 4{,}962$

**5.** $13.91
$+\ 45.46$

**6.**   7,207
$+\ \ \ 894$

**7.**   605
$-\ 356$

**8.**   6,300
$-\ 5{,}022$

Name _____

# Estimating Quotients

Estimate each quotient.

**1.** $5\overline{)98.65}$      **2.** $11\overline{)123.52}$      **3.** $73\overline{)787.42}$      **4.** $17\overline{)34.25}$

**5.** $5.2\overline{)4,120.5}$      **6.** $5.7\overline{)12,500.3}$      **7.** $28\overline{)159.73}$      **8.** $12\overline{)987.43}$

**9.** $3,156 \div 62.5$      **10.** $489.95 \div 7.1$      **11.** $3,720.3 \div 12.3$      **12.** $130.71 \div 4.5$

_____    _____    _____    _____

Estimate. Then use your estimate to choose the letter of the exact quotient.

**13.** $0.12\overline{)40.8}$     **14.** $359.03 \div 9.2$     **15.** $0.72\overline{)424.8}$     **16.** $255.6 \div 0.48$

   **a.** 34            **a.** 39.025         **a.** 59.3          **a.** 53.25

   **b.** 340          **b.** 390.25         **b.** 5,900        **b.** 532.5

   **c.** 3.4           **c.** 3902.5         **c.** 590          **c.** 5325

Circle the letter of the phrase that completes each statement.

**17.** $0.71\overline{)22.3}$ is       **18.** $88.5 \div 1.00$ is       **19.** $33.9 \div 5.7$ is

   **a.** less than 22.3.       **a.** less than 88.5.       **a.** less than 33.9.

   **b.** equal to 22.3.        **b.** equal to 88.5.        **b.** equal to 33.9.

   **c.** greater than 22.3.    **c.** greater than 88.5.    **c.** greater than 33.9.

## Review and Remember

Add, subtract, multiply, or divide.

**1.**    9.6          **2.**   $8.38         **3.**   1.25          **4.**   $5.91
   $\underline{+\ 8.3}$        $\underline{+\ 2.17}$      $\underline{-\ 0.52}$      $\underline{-\ 2.40}$

**5.**    289          **6.**   5,681        **7.**   734         **8.**   $2.58
   $\underline{\times\ \ \ 3}$         $\underline{\times\ \ \ \ 3}$      $\underline{\times\ 18}$       $\underline{\times\ 25}$

**9.** $7\overline{)8,337}$      **10.** $5\overline{)9,480}$      **11.** $6\overline{)894}$      **12.** $7\overline{)812}$

          

Name _____

## Collecting Data

Mr. Conrad's sixth-grade class collected information
about their families, using this survey.

> ## Tell us about your family
> 1. Do you have any pets?
> 2. Do you take turns cooking meals?
> 3. How many meals each week do you cook?
> 4. How far away from school do you live?
> 5. How many hours each day does your family
>    watch television?
> 6. How many brothers do you have?
> 7. How many sisters do you have?

Use the survey to answer the following questions.

**1.** Which of the questions will have numerical answers? _____

**2.** Which questions will not have numerical answers? _____

**3.** For what questions would the range be useful data? _____

**4.** For what questions would the mode be useful data? _____

## Review and Remember

Add. Estimate to check each answer.

| | | | | | | | |
|---|---|---|---|---|---|---|---|
| **1.** 235,741 | | **2.** 437,926 | | **3.** 896,541 | | **4.** 650,721 | |
| + 843,167 | | + 437,926 | | + 65,430 | | + 198,430 | |

**5.** 8.88     **6.** 250,978     **7.** 983     **8.** 6.75
   +1.11        + 2,345       + 96       + 0.25

# Describing Data

Find the range, mode, median, and mean for each.

**1.**

| COST OF HAMBURGER | |
|---|---|
| Mack's | $ 0.78 |
| RR's | 1.19 |
| King's | 1.04 |
| Club's | 2.95 |
| Joe's | 1.19 |

**2.**

| MATH TEST SCORES | |
|---|---|
| Bart | 76 |
| Ana | 68 |
| Lucia | 90 |
| Harry | 90 |
| Sally | 74 |

**3.**

| JEFF'S DART SCORES | |
|---|---|
| Game 1 | 102 |
| Game 2 | 120 |
| Game 3 | 112 |
| Game 4 | 118 |
| Game 5 | 94 |
| Game 6 | 102 |

range _____     range _____     range _____

mode _____     mode _____     mode _____

median _____     median _____     median _____

mean _____     mean _____     mean _____

Use a calculator and guess-and-check method to find each missing number.

**4.** The mean of three numbers is 9. The mode is 7. What are the three numbers?

_____

**5.** The mean of two numbers is 25. The range is 10. What are the two numbers?

_____

**6.** The median of five numbers is 15. The mode is 6. The mean is 12. What are the five numbers?

_____

**7.** The mean of two numbers is 32. The range is 18. What are the two numbers?

_____

## Review and Remember

Solve.

| **1.** | **2.** | **3.** | **4.** | **5.** |
|---|---|---|---|---|
| 275<br>+ 303 | 456<br>− 327 | 2,653<br>+ 1,245 | 762<br>× 3 | 589<br>× 8 |

Name _____

# Making and Interpreting Graphs

Use the pictograph to answer Problems 1–3.

**1.** How many apples were sold?

_____

**2.** What is the range of the data?

_____

**3.** How many more pears were sold than bananas?

_____

| TOM'S FRESH FRUIT SALES | |
|---|---|
| Bananas | |
| Apples | |
| Pears | |
| Oranges | |

Each symbol equals 10 pieces of fruit.

Use the chart to answer Problems 4–6.

**4.** If you were to make a double bar graph, what would you label each axis?

_____

**5.** What scale would you use on the vertical axis?

_____

**6.** Draw a key to be used with the graph.

_____

| BOOK CLUB POINTS EARNED | | |
|---|---|---|
| Student | Last Month | This Month |
| Georgia | 210 | 325 |
| Darrell | 290 | 495 |
| Carla | 325 | 275 |
| John | 410 | 315 |

## Review and Remember

Subtract. Use mental math, paper and pencil, or a calculator. Estimate to check each answer.

**1.** 841 − 114

**2.** 17,620 − 9,855

**3.** 687 − 90

**4.** $38.73 − 17.04

**5.** 9,462 − 8,076

**6.** 236.25 − 65.08

**7.** $15.00 − $8.95 _____

**8.** 2.109 − 0.17 _____

**9.** 400 − 167 _____

**10.** 26,217 − 8,050 _____

© Silver Burdett Ginn Inc.

Name _____

# Making Bar Graphs

**1.** Using the data in the table, complete the bar graph.

| VILLAGE MIDDLE SCHOOL SIXTH-GRADE BOYS' FAVORITE SPORTS | |
| --- | --- |
| Baseball | 47 |
| Track | 35 |
| Soccer | 86 |
| Basketball | 32 |

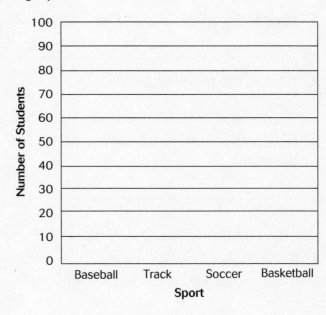

**2.** Draw a graph that will minimize the differences in popularity among the sports.

## Review and Remember

Add, subtract, multiply, or divide.

**1.**   4.3
       + 9.7

**2.**   7.43
       + 9.76

**3.**   46.85
       −  9.70

**4.**   546.73
       −  92.14

**5.**   212
       × 31

**6.**   611
       × 57

**7.**   83)1,416

**8.**   76)14,744

# Making Stem-and-Leaf Plots

Mr. George was grading math tests. He made the chart at the right. Use the data in the chart to answer each question.

**1.** What is the greatest value? _____

**2.** What is the least value? _____

**3.** List all the values that you would use as stems in a stem-and-leaf plot.

_____

**4.** Which score appears most often in the data? _____

**5.** Make a stem-and-leaf plot for the data.

| Grade | Score | Number of students |
|---|---|---|
| A | 98 | 1 |
| | 95 | 2 |
| | 93 | 1 |
| | 91 | 1 |
| B | 87 | 5 |
| | 86 | 3 |
| | 82 | 1 |
| | 80 | 2 |
| C | 79 | 3 |
| | 77 | 3 |
| | 72 | 2 |
| | 71 | 3 |
| D | 68 | 2 |
| | 67 | 2 |
| | 65 | 1 |
| | 60 | 1 |
| | 55 | 1 |

## Review and Remember

Add, subtract, multiply, or divide.

**1.**  231.56
    + 40.3

**2.**  5,993.046
    + 324.8

**3.**  455.424
    − 387.069

**4.**  29.0896
    − 0.5442

**5.**  38.6
    × 5.4

**6.**  27.63
    × 4.08

**7.**  2)59.14

**8.**  3)73.56

Name _____

# Using Exponents

Use a calculator to complete the table.

| | Number | Product of Sevens | Number of Sevens | Number Using Exponents |
|---|---|---|---|---|
| **1.** | 7 | 7 | 1 | |
| **2.** | 49 | $7 \times 7$ | 2 | |
| **3.** | | $7 \times 7 \times 7$ | | |
| **4.** | 2,401 | | | |
| **5.** | | | | $7^5$ |
| **6.** | | $7 \times 7 \times 7 \times 7 \times 7 \times 7$ | | |
| **7.** | | | 7 | |
| **8.** | 5,764,801 | | | |

Write each expression in standard form.

**9.** $10^3 = $ _____  **10.** $5^5 = $ _____  **11.** $8^4 = $ _____  **12.** $9^2 = $ _____

Write each expression in exponent form.

**13.** $15 \times 15 \times 15 = $ _____  **14.** $4 \times 4 \times 4 \times 4 = $ _____

**15.** $19 \times 19 = $ _____  **16.** $12 \times 12 \times 12 = $ _____

## Review and Remember

Write the value of the underlined digit.

**1.** 7̲0,264 _____  **2.** 141,2̲15 _____

**3.** 14.04̲ _____  **4.** 7.017̲ _____

**5.** 7,2̲51 _____  **6.** 0.85̲9 _____

**7.** 10.1̲7 _____  **8.** 2̲,347,116 _____

Name _____

# Finding Prime and Composite Numbers

List all the factors of each number. Then write *prime* or *composite* for each number.

**1.** 6 _____

**2.** 15 _____

**3.** 47 _____

**4.** 77 _____

**5.** 39 _____

**6.** 43 _____

Each of these is a composite number. Use divisibility rules to find more than two factors, other than 1 and the number itself, for each.

**7.** 230 _____

**8.** 8,640 _____

**9.** 9,669 _____

**10.** 14,332 _____

**11.** 57,033 _____

**12.** 2,816 _____

Write *true* or *false*.

**13.** Composite numbers can be even or odd numbers. _____

**14.** The number 1 is a prime number. _____

**15.** All prime numbers are odd numbers. _____

**16.** A factor of every even number is 2. _____

## Review and Remember

Solve. Estimate to be sure your answer is reasonable.

**1.** $\begin{array}{r} 8,975 \\ + 2,053 \\ \hline \end{array}$

**2.** $\begin{array}{r} 6,275 \\ + 2,309 \\ \hline \end{array}$

**3.** $\begin{array}{r} 4,156 \\ - \phantom{0}39 \\ \hline \end{array}$

**4.** $\begin{array}{r} 61,350 \\ - 14,271 \\ \hline \end{array}$

**5.** 9,678 + 2,421 = _____

**6.** 7,557 − 5,775 = _____

**7.** $\begin{array}{r} 34.4 \\ \times \phantom{0}4.6 \\ \hline \end{array}$

**8.** $\begin{array}{r} 0.58 \\ \times \phantom{0}3.9 \\ \hline \end{array}$

**9.** $22\overline{)1.76}$

**10.** $9\overline{)26.37}$

# Finding the Greatest Common Factor

Find all the factors of each.

**1.** 8 _____     **2.** 12 _____

**3.** 13 _____     **4.** 16 _____

**5.** 18 _____     **6.** 24 _____

Use your answers above to find the GCF.

**7.** 8, 12 _____    **8.** 12, 13 _____    **9.** 8, 16 _____    **10.** 12, 18 _____

**11.** 12, 16 _____    **12.** 16, 24 _____    **13.** 12, 24 _____    **14.** 8, 24 _____

Write the first 10 non-zero multiples of each.

**15.** 2 _____

**16.** 3 _____

**17.** 6 _____

**18.** 9 _____

**19.** 7 _____

## Review and Remember

Complete each table.

Rule: Subtract 1.575

|  | Input | Output |
|---|---|---|
| **1.** | 5.902 | |
| **2.** | | 85.015 |
| **3.** | 250.75 | |

Rule: Subtract 8.245

|  | Input | Output |
|---|---|---|
| **4.** | 123.85 | |
| **5.** | | 0.55 |
| **6.** | 8.903 | |

   

# Mixed Numbers and Least Common Multiple

Write the missing numerator or denominator.

**1.** $\dfrac{2}{3} = \dfrac{\square}{9}$

**2.** $\dfrac{1}{2} = \dfrac{4}{\square}$

**3.** $\dfrac{4}{5} = \dfrac{\square\square}{15}$

**4.** $\dfrac{8}{\square\square} = \dfrac{16}{20}$

**5.** $\dfrac{5}{8} = \dfrac{\square\square}{56}$

**6.** $\dfrac{42}{49} = \dfrac{\square}{7}$

**7.** $\dfrac{1}{4} = \dfrac{13}{\square\square}$

**8.** $\dfrac{65}{\square\square\square} = \dfrac{13}{20}$

Write each fraction as a mixed number or a whole number.

**9.** $\dfrac{3}{2} = $ _____

**10.** $\dfrac{9}{4} = $ _____

**11.** $\dfrac{13}{5} = $ _____

**12.** $\dfrac{30}{7} = $ _____

**13.** $\dfrac{16}{4} = $ _____

**14.** $\dfrac{49}{7} = $ _____

**15.** $\dfrac{73}{8} = $ _____

**16.** $\dfrac{12}{3} = $ _____

**17.** $\dfrac{43}{6} = $ _____

**18.** $\dfrac{27}{10} = $ _____

Write as an improper fraction.

**19.** $2\dfrac{1}{4} = $ ___

**20.** $3\dfrac{1}{3} = $ ___

**21.** $1\dfrac{7}{8} = $ ___

**22.** $3\dfrac{2}{5} = $ ___

**23.** $5\dfrac{3}{8} = $ ___

**24.** $6\dfrac{1}{5} = $ ___

**25.** $9\dfrac{2}{7} = $ ___

**26.** $4\dfrac{11}{13} = $ ___

**27.** $12\dfrac{1}{10} = $ ___

**28.** $9\dfrac{2}{12} = $ ___

Find the least common multiple for each set of numbers.

**29.** 2, 3 _____

**30.** 6, 7 _____

**31.** 2, 3, 6 _____

**32.** 3, 6, 9 _____

## Review and Remember

Solve. Round each quotient to the nearest hundredth.

**1.** $8\overline{)5.321}$

**2.** $26 \div 3 = $ _____

**3.** $4\overline{)7.09}$

Find each sum or difference.

**4.** $32.8 + 5.77 = $ _____

**5.** $48.8 - 7.11 = $ _____

**6.** $15.8 + 33 = $ _____

Name _____

# Writing Like Fractions and Comparing Fractions

Find the LCD. Then use the LCD to write like fractions.

1. $\frac{1}{2}$, $\frac{1}{3}$ _____

2. $\frac{3}{4}$, $\frac{2}{3}$ _____

3. $\frac{1}{5}$, $\frac{3}{10}$ _____

4. $\frac{3}{4}$, $\frac{5}{8}$ _____

5. $\frac{5}{6}$, $\frac{7}{8}$ _____

6. $\frac{3}{5}$, $\frac{9}{10}$ _____

Compare. Write >, <, or = in each ◯.

7. $\frac{3}{4}$ ◯ $\frac{2}{3}$

8. $\frac{1}{2}$ ◯ $\frac{3}{5}$

9. $\frac{5}{6}$ ◯ $\frac{7}{9}$

10. $\frac{3}{5}$ ◯ $\frac{2}{3}$

11. $\frac{6}{9}$ ◯ $\frac{2}{3}$

12. $\frac{3}{8}$ ◯ $\frac{1}{4}$

13. $\frac{3}{4}$ ◯ $\frac{4}{7}$

14. $\frac{3}{7}$ ◯ $\frac{1}{2}$

15. $\frac{1}{3}$ ◯ $\frac{5}{8}$

16. $2\frac{3}{5}$ ◯ $2\frac{5}{8}$

17. $1\frac{5}{10}$ ◯ $1\frac{1}{2}$

18. $5\frac{10}{25}$ ◯ $5\frac{3}{5}$

List in order from least to greatest.

19. $\frac{5}{13}$ $\frac{9}{13}$ $\frac{7}{13}$ _____

20. $\frac{4}{5}$ $\frac{4}{11}$ $\frac{4}{8}$ _____

21. $2\frac{2}{5}$ $2\frac{3}{10}$ $1\frac{8}{9}$ _____

22. $2\frac{2}{5}$ $3\frac{1}{5}$ $1\frac{3}{5}$ _____

## Review and Remember

Add, subtract, or multiply.

1.  $\begin{array}{r} 7,536 \\ + 4,971 \\ \hline \end{array}$

2.  $\begin{array}{r} 6,028 \\ + 3,743 \\ \hline \end{array}$

3.  $\begin{array}{r} 347,251 \\ + 256,796 \\ \hline \end{array}$

4.  $\begin{array}{r} 905,675 \\ + 247,421 \\ \hline \end{array}$

5.  $\begin{array}{r} 3,468 \\ - 1,292 \\ \hline \end{array}$

6.  $\begin{array}{r} 34,539 \\ - 22,354 \\ \hline \end{array}$

7.  $\begin{array}{r} 563,204 \\ - 271,583 \\ \hline \end{array}$

8.  $\begin{array}{r} 347,060 \\ - 35,231 \\ \hline \end{array}$

9.  $\begin{array}{r} 324 \\ \times 24 \\ \hline \end{array}$

10.  $\begin{array}{r} \$4.53 \\ \times 36 \\ \hline \end{array}$

11.  $\begin{array}{r} 7,891 \\ \times 79 \\ \hline \end{array}$

12.  $\begin{array}{r} 2,790 \\ \times 87 \\ \hline \end{array}$

Name _____

# Adding and Subtracting Fractions With Like Denominators

Add. Write each sum in simplest form.

**1.** $\frac{2}{3}$
$+\frac{1}{3}$

**2.** $\frac{1}{5}$
$+\frac{3}{5}$

**3.** $\frac{1}{4}$
$+\frac{2}{4}$

**4.** $\frac{1}{8}$
$+\frac{3}{8}$

**5.** $\frac{2}{5}$
$+\frac{1}{5}$

**6.** $\frac{1}{12}$
$+\frac{4}{12}$

**7.** $\frac{1}{6}$
$+\frac{1}{6}$

**8.** $\frac{2}{3}$
$+\frac{5}{3}$

Subtract. Write each answer in simplest form.

**9.** $\frac{4}{6}$
$-\frac{2}{6}$

**10.** $\frac{9}{10}$
$-\frac{2}{10}$

**11.** $\frac{5}{6}$
$-\frac{2}{6}$

**12.** $\frac{5}{12}$
$-\frac{5}{12}$

**13.** $\frac{3}{5} - \frac{2}{5} =$ _____

**14.** $\frac{9}{10} - \frac{4}{10} =$ _____

**15.** $\frac{11}{18} - \frac{6}{18} =$ _____

**16.** $\frac{10}{4} - \frac{9}{4} =$ _____

## Review and Remember

Complete.

**1.** Circle the numbers that are divisible by 9.

   15      36      216      105      117

**2.** Circle the factors of 64.

   1       5       8       12       16

**3.** Circle the multiples of 4.

   4       7       11       27       64

# Estimating With Fractions

Round each fraction to 0, $\frac{1}{2}$, or 1.

**1.** $\frac{1}{12}$ _____

**2.** $\frac{8}{9}$ _____

**3.** $\frac{7}{15}$ _____

**4.** $\frac{10}{9}$ _____

Estimate each sum or difference.

**5.** $\frac{2}{3} + \frac{1}{4}$ _____

**6.** $\frac{7}{10} - \frac{1}{3}$ _____

**7.** $\frac{8}{14} + \frac{1}{2}$ _____

**8.** $2\frac{1}{4} + 3\frac{7}{8}$ _____

**9.** $4\frac{3}{4} - 1\frac{7}{16}$ _____

**10.** $7\frac{5}{6} + 12\frac{11}{13}$ _____

**11.** $9\frac{7}{8} - 2\frac{3}{5}$ _____

**12.** $16\frac{1}{9} - \frac{2}{3}$ _____

**13.** $9\frac{11}{16} + 2\frac{4}{9}$ _____

Solve.

**14.** Mrs. Scott has $9\frac{2}{3}$ yards of fabric. She needs $6\frac{1}{8}$ yards to make a blouse. About how much fabric will she have left?

_____

**15.** Lori jogged $\frac{9}{10}$ mile on Monday, $1\frac{3}{4}$ miles on Wednesday, and $3\frac{2}{5}$ miles on Friday. About how many miles did she jog altogether?

_____

## Review and Remember

Solve.

**1.** $\begin{array}{r} 0.027 \\ + 0.063 \\ \hline \end{array}$

**2.** $\begin{array}{r} 3.3642 \\ + 4.2891 \\ \hline \end{array}$

**3.** $\begin{array}{r} 0.136 \\ - 0.085 \\ \hline \end{array}$

**4.** $\begin{array}{r} 5.9863 \\ - 0.378 \\ \hline \end{array}$

**5.** $3.5\overline{)7.21}$

**6.** $0.62\overline{)0.434}$

**7.** $6.2\overline{)17.36}$

**8.** $1.6\overline{)35.6}$

Name _____

# Adding and Subtracting Fractions

Add or subtract. Write each answer in simplest form.

1. $\dfrac{1}{5}$
$+\dfrac{3}{5}$

2. $\dfrac{9}{10}$
$-\dfrac{3}{10}$

3. $\dfrac{1}{3}$
$+\dfrac{3}{4}$

4. $\dfrac{3}{8}$
$+\dfrac{1}{2}$

5. $\dfrac{3}{10}$
$-\dfrac{1}{4}$

6. $\dfrac{4}{7}$
$+\dfrac{1}{4}$

7. $\dfrac{7}{9}$
$-\dfrac{2}{3}$

8. $\dfrac{3}{4}$
$-\dfrac{2}{5}$

9. $\dfrac{7}{10}$
$+\dfrac{3}{5}$

10. $\dfrac{1}{2}$
$-\dfrac{3}{7}$

Estimate first. Then find the actual sum or difference.

11. $\dfrac{4}{9}+\dfrac{2}{3}=$ _____

12. $\dfrac{3}{5}-\dfrac{1}{4}=$ _____

13. $\dfrac{8}{9}-\dfrac{2}{3}=$ _____

14. $\dfrac{5}{7}-\dfrac{1}{14}=$ _____

15. $\dfrac{7}{15}+\dfrac{3}{5}=$ _____

16. $\dfrac{19}{20}-\dfrac{3}{5}=$ _____

17. It took Mary $\dfrac{1}{2}$ hour to get to Chicago from Oak Park. It took Dennis $\dfrac{1}{4}$ hour to get to Chicago from Riverside. How much longer did it take Mary to get to Chicago than Dennis?

18. Mark is a pizza baker. He used $6\dfrac{1}{3}$ ounces of tomato sauce on a medium pizza and $8\dfrac{1}{3}$ ounces of sauce on a large pizza. How much sauce did he use altogether?

## Review and Remember

Write the prime factorization for each number.

1. 42

2. 36

3. 64

© Silver Burdett Ginn Inc.

Use after Grade 6, text page 203. **23**

# Subtracting Mixed Numbers With Renaming

Rename each mixed number.

**1.** $3\frac{3}{4} = 2\frac{\boxed{\phantom{0}}}{4}$

**2.** $3\frac{2}{8} = 2\frac{\boxed{\phantom{0}}}{8}$

**3.** $5\frac{1}{3} = 4\frac{\boxed{\phantom{0}}}{3}$

Subtract. Write each answer in simplest form.

**4.**   $18$
    $-\ 6\frac{3}{4}$

**5.**   $9\frac{1}{4}$
    $-\ 2\frac{7}{8}$

**6.**   $13\frac{1}{2}$
    $-\ 9\frac{9}{10}$

**7.**   $15\frac{3}{8}$
    $-\ 7\frac{9}{16}$

**8.**   $6\frac{1}{2}$
    $-\ 1\frac{2}{3}$

**9.**   $9\frac{7}{8}$
    $-\ 2\frac{9}{10}$

**10.**   $13\frac{6}{7}$
    $-\ 6\frac{1}{3}$

**11.**   $16\frac{1}{9}$
    $-\ \frac{2}{3}$

**12.** $14 - 7\frac{5}{6} =$ _____

**13.** $8\frac{1}{8} - 5\frac{7}{10} =$ _____

Solve.

**14.** Debbie used $2\frac{3}{4}$ cups of flour for one bread recipe and $3\frac{1}{8}$ cups for another. How much more flour did she use for one recipe than the other?

_____

**15.** Kris worked 7 hours on Monday and $4\frac{1}{2}$ hours on Wednesday. How much longer did she work on Monday than on Wednesday?

_____

## Review and Remember

Add, subtract, multiply, or divide.

**1.**   $6.113$
    $+\ 7.418$

**2.**   $7.6$
    $-\ 5.6222$

**3.**   $4.353$
    $-\ 1.234$

**4.**   $3.507$
    $+\ 17.31$

**5.** $3.455 \times 500$ _____

**6.** $22 \times 3,000$ _____

**7.** $4,900 \div 70$ _____

**8.** $7,200 \div 9$ _____

# Adding and Subtracting Fractions and Mixed Numbers

Add or subtract. Write each answer in simplest form.

1.  $\frac{2}{5}$
    $+ \frac{2}{5}$

2.  $\frac{15}{16}$
    $- \frac{5}{16}$

3.  $\frac{7}{10}$
    $- \frac{1}{2}$

4.  $\frac{1}{3}$
    $+ \frac{2}{9}$

5.  $\frac{2}{3}$
    $+ \frac{5}{6}$

6.  $\frac{2}{3}$
    $- \frac{3}{8}$

7.  $\frac{5}{12}$
    $+ \frac{5}{6}$

8.  $\frac{4}{9}$
    $- \frac{1}{3}$

9.  $4\frac{1}{4}$
    $+ 2\frac{1}{2}$

10. $8\frac{4}{9}$
    $- 5\frac{2}{3}$

11. $6\frac{1}{8}$
    $+ 3\frac{3}{4}$

12. $2\frac{1}{6}$
    $- 1\frac{2}{3}$

13. $1\frac{1}{3}$
    $- \frac{1}{6}$

14. $5\frac{1}{7}$
    $- 2\frac{1}{4}$

15. $3\frac{1}{6}$
    $- 1\frac{1}{4}$

16. $6\frac{1}{8}$
    $+ 2\frac{1}{4}$

## Review and Remember

Circle the letter for the best estimate.

1. The Hanson family is traveling by car on their vacation. On the first day, they planned to average 46 miles per hour for about 7 hours. Which range gives the best estimate of their miles traveled?

   **a.** 280 to 350 miles

   **b.** 100 to 250 miles

   **c.** 350 to 450 miles

2. On their second day, the Hanson family planned to travel only 6 hours at an average speed of 55 miles per hour. Which range gives the best estimate of their miles traveled?

   **a.** 200 to 300 miles

   **b.** 350 to 450 miles

   **c.** 300 to 360 miles

# Multiplying Fractions

Multiply. Write each answer in simplest form.

**1.** $\frac{7}{9} \times \frac{3}{5} =$ _____

**2.** $\frac{2}{3} \times \frac{4}{5} =$ _____

**3.** $\frac{3}{14} \times \frac{7}{10} =$ _____

**4.** $\frac{4}{5} \times \frac{2}{5} =$ _____

**5.** $\frac{5}{6} \times \frac{7}{10} =$ _____

**6.** $\frac{3}{10} \times \frac{7}{10} =$ _____

**7.** $\frac{5}{8} \times \frac{3}{20} =$ _____

**8.** $\frac{3}{5} \times \frac{1}{9} =$ _____

**9.** $\frac{3}{4} \times \frac{2}{5} =$ _____

**10.** $\frac{2}{3} \times \frac{3}{5} =$ _____

**11.** $\frac{3}{10} \times \frac{5}{6} =$ _____

**12.** $\frac{1}{4} \times \frac{2}{5} =$ _____

Find each missing number.

**13.** $\frac{2}{3} \times \frac{n}{4} = \frac{10}{12}$   $n =$ _____

**14.** $\frac{c}{2} \times \frac{3}{5} = \frac{3}{10}$   $c =$ _____

**15.** $3 \times \frac{a}{4} = \frac{3}{4}$   $a =$ _____

**16.** $\frac{2}{3} \times \frac{3}{m} = \frac{6}{15}$   $m =$ _____

Write *true* or *false*. If false, write $>$, $<$, or $=$ to make the sentence true.

**17.** $\frac{3}{4} \times \frac{2}{3} < \frac{1}{2}$ _____

**18.** $\frac{13}{14} \times \frac{1}{2} > \frac{13}{14}$ _____

**19.** $\frac{3}{8} \times \frac{4}{5} > \frac{3}{8}$ _____

**20.** $\frac{5}{7} \times \frac{5}{7} < \frac{5}{7}$ _____

## Review and Remember

Add, subtract, multiply, or divide.

**1.** $\frac{2}{11}$
$+ \frac{6}{11}$

**2.** $\frac{4}{8}$
$+ \frac{3}{8}$

**3.** $\frac{1}{6}$
$+ \frac{2}{3}$

**4.** $\frac{7}{7}$
$- \frac{7}{7}$

**5.** $\frac{3}{4}$
$- \frac{1}{2}$

**6.** $2.7$
$\times\ 6$

**7.** $0.82$
$\times\ 1.4$

**8.** $7\overline{)9.352}$

**9.** $6\overline{)79.86}$

**10.** $7\overline{)2.471}$

# Multiplying Fractions and Mixed Numbers

Multiply. Write each answer in simplest form.
Estimate to be sure your answers are reasonable.

**1.** $2\frac{2}{5} \times 2 =$ _____

**2.** $\frac{1}{7} \times 3\frac{1}{2} =$ _____

**3.** $1\frac{3}{4} \times 6 =$ _____

**4.** $1\frac{3}{5} \times 2 =$ _____

**5.** $3\frac{1}{5} \times \frac{1}{4} =$ _____

**6.** $5\frac{1}{3} \times \frac{3}{16} =$ _____

**7.** $5\frac{1}{4} \times \frac{1}{7} =$ _____

**8.** $\frac{7}{12} \times 3\frac{3}{7} =$ _____

**9.** $3 \times 4\frac{4}{5} =$ _____

**10.** $\frac{5}{6} \times 2\frac{1}{7} =$ _____

**11.** $\frac{2}{5} \times 6\frac{1}{4} =$ _____

**12.** $10 \times \frac{2}{5} =$ _____

**13.** $1\frac{1}{4} \times \frac{2}{3} =$ _____

**14.** $\frac{2}{5} \times 2\frac{1}{2} =$ _____

**15.** $5 \times 3\frac{1}{10} =$ _____

**16.** $2\frac{1}{6} \times \frac{2}{3} =$ _____

**17.** $4\frac{2}{7} \times 2 =$ _____

**18.** $\frac{1}{2} \times 2\frac{1}{3} =$ _____

**19.** $4 \times 7\frac{1}{5} =$ _____

**20.** $8 \times 6\frac{1}{4} =$ _____

**21.** $16 \times \frac{3}{8} =$ _____

**22.** $\frac{1}{3} \times 1\frac{1}{4} =$ _____

**23.** $7 \times 1\frac{2}{3} =$ _____

**24.** $2\frac{1}{2} \times \frac{4}{5} =$ _____

Evaluate, using order of operations.

**25.** $5\frac{1}{2} \times \frac{1}{3} + \frac{1}{6} =$ _____

**26.** $7\frac{3}{8} - 3\frac{1}{2} \times \frac{2}{7} =$ _____

**27.** $2\frac{4}{5} + 4\frac{1}{5} \times \frac{2}{3} =$ _____

**28.** $1\frac{1}{3} \times \frac{3}{4} - \frac{1}{2} =$ _____

**29.** $3\frac{1}{8} - \frac{1}{2} \times \frac{3}{4} -$ _____

**30.** $6\frac{1}{6} \times \frac{6}{7} + 1\frac{1}{4} =$ _____

## Review and Remember

**1.** Circle the prime numbers.

16   7   55   17   21

**2.** Circle the composite numbers.

4  11  47  63  75

**3.** Circle the factors of 32.

3     1     8     7     11

**4.** Circle the multiples of 12.

4  30  12  60  24

Name _____

# Estimating Products

Estimate each product.

**1.** $\frac{7}{8} \times 5 =$ _____

**2.** $2\frac{3}{5} \times 2\frac{1}{5} =$ _____

**3.** $2\frac{9}{10} \times 6\frac{4}{5} =$ _____

**4.** $20 \times \frac{2}{3} =$ _____

**5.** $23 \times \frac{5}{12} =$ _____

**6.** $5\frac{11}{12} \times 4\frac{1}{5} =$ _____

**7.** $7 \times 2\frac{2}{3} =$ _____

**8.** $1\frac{5}{6} \times \frac{7}{8} =$ _____

**9.** $\frac{5}{6} \times 10\frac{1}{10} =$ _____

**10.** $2\frac{5}{8} \times 3\frac{1}{3} =$ _____

**11.** $9\frac{1}{8} \times 4\frac{1}{9} =$ _____

**12.** $\frac{3}{7} \times 34 =$ _____

**13.** $5 \times 3\frac{1}{6} =$ _____

**14.** $2\frac{1}{3} \times 1\frac{2}{3} =$ _____

**15.** $\frac{7}{10} \times 40 =$ _____

Estimate to choose the most reasonable answer.

**16.** $\frac{4}{5}$ of 11
 **a.** less than 6
 **b.** greater than 6

**17.** $4 \times 2\frac{5}{8}$
 **a.** less than 10
 **b.** greater than 10

**18.** $10 \times 2\frac{5}{8}$
 **a.** less than 30
 **b.** greater than 30

**19.** $\frac{3}{4}$ of 24
 **a.** less than 12
 **b.** greater than 12

**20.** $\frac{5}{9}$ of 4
 **a.** less than 2
 **b.** greater than 2

**21.** $4\frac{2}{5} \times 2\frac{1}{4}$
 **a.** less than 8
 **b.** greater than 8

# Review and Remember

Solve. Write each fraction in simplest form.

**1.** $\begin{array}{r} \frac{4}{5} \\ + \frac{3}{5} \\ \hline \end{array}$

**2.** $\begin{array}{r} 2\frac{7}{8} \\ + 6\frac{5}{8} \\ \hline \end{array}$

**3.** $\begin{array}{r} 8\frac{1}{5} \\ - 7\frac{2}{5} \\ \hline \end{array}$

**4.** $\begin{array}{r} 5\frac{7}{10} \\ - 2\frac{4}{5} \\ \hline \end{array}$

**5.** $\begin{array}{r} 8.5 \\ \times 4.5 \\ \hline \end{array}$

**6.** $\begin{array}{r} 1.44 \\ \times 7.2 \\ \hline \end{array}$

**7.** $5\overline{)1,507}$

**8.** $35\overline{)7,076}$

© Silver Burdett Ginn Inc.

# Dividing Fractions

Write the reciprocal of each.

**1.** $\frac{5}{6}$ _____  **2.** $\frac{1}{4}$ _____  **3.** $6$ _____  **4.** $2\frac{2}{3}$ _____

**5.** $\frac{10}{3}$ _____  **6.** $4\frac{7}{8}$ _____  **7.** $22$ _____  **8.** $\frac{9}{5}$ _____

Divide. Write each answer in simplest form. Check by multiplying.

**9.** $\frac{2}{5} \div \frac{1}{2} =$ _____  **10.** $\frac{1}{7} \div \frac{2}{3} =$ _____  **11.** $\frac{1}{2} \div \frac{1}{8} =$ _____

**12.** $5 \div \frac{5}{6} =$ _____  **13.** $7 \div \frac{2}{5} =$ _____  **14.** $\frac{3}{5} \div \frac{7}{8} =$ _____

Follow the rule to find each missing number.

Rule: Divide by $\frac{1}{2}$

| | Input | Output |
|---|---|---|
| **15.** | $2$ | |
| **16.** | $\frac{1}{5}$ | |
| **17.** | $\frac{4}{3}$ | |

Rule: Divide by $\frac{3}{4}$

| | Input | Output |
|---|---|---|
| **18.** | $\frac{1}{4}$ | |
| **19.** | $6$ | |
| **20.** | $2$ | |

Rule: Divide by $\frac{1}{10}$

| | Input | Output |
|---|---|---|
| **21.** | $\frac{3}{10}$ | |
| **22.** | $4$ | |
| **23.** | $5$ | |

## Review and Remember

Write each answer in simplest form.

**1.** $\begin{array}{r} \frac{1}{3} \\ + \frac{1}{4} \\ \hline \end{array}$   **2.** $\begin{array}{r} 6\frac{1}{2} \\ + 3\frac{2}{5} \\ \hline \end{array}$   **3.** $\begin{array}{r} \frac{5}{8} \\ - \frac{1}{4} \\ \hline \end{array}$   **4.** $\begin{array}{r} 14\frac{1}{5} \\ - 7\frac{7}{10} \\ \hline \end{array}$

**5.** $\frac{2}{3} - \frac{1}{6}$ _____  **6.** $1\frac{1}{4} + 4\frac{1}{3}$ _____  **7.** $\frac{3}{4} - \frac{1}{6}$ _____

# Dividing Fractions and Mixed Numbers

Divide. Write each answer in simplest form. Check by multiplying.

**1.** $9 \div \frac{1}{3} =$ _____

**2.** $\frac{3}{8} \div \frac{5}{6} =$ _____

**3.** $\frac{2}{3} \div \frac{7}{8} =$ _____

**4.** $\frac{2}{5} \div \frac{1}{3} =$ _____

**5.** $\frac{3}{4} \div \frac{3}{4} =$ _____

**6.** $12 \div \frac{1}{2} =$ _____

**7.** $\frac{1}{2} \div \frac{3}{4} =$ _____

**8.** $3 \div \frac{2}{5} =$ _____

**9.** $\frac{1}{7} \div \frac{3}{7} =$ _____

**10.** $4\frac{1}{3} \div \frac{5}{6} =$ _____

**11.** $6\frac{3}{4} \div \frac{9}{10} =$ _____

**12.** $5\frac{1}{2} \div \frac{1}{2} =$ _____

**13.** $8 \div 2\frac{1}{2} =$ _____

**14.** $3\frac{1}{3} \div 1\frac{1}{10} =$ _____

**15.** $\frac{3}{8} \div 1\frac{2}{3} =$ _____

**16.** $6\frac{5}{7} \div 4 =$ _____

**17.** $1\frac{1}{8} \div \frac{3}{8} =$ _____

**18.** $2\frac{3}{5} \div \frac{1}{5} =$ _____

Divide. Write each quotient three ways.

**19.** $18\overline{)4,545}$ _____

**20.** $10\overline{)298}$ _____

**21.** $\frac{45}{6}$ _____

**22.** $\frac{189}{36}$ _____

**23.** $775 \div 10$ _____

**24.** $90 \div 12$ _____

## Review and Remember

Add, subtract, multiply, or divide. Write each fraction in simplest form.

**1.** $\begin{aligned} 8\frac{3}{4} \\ + 4\frac{2}{3} \\ \hline \end{aligned}$

**2.** $\begin{aligned} 3\frac{4}{5} \\ + 6\frac{6}{10} \\ \hline \end{aligned}$

**3.** $\begin{aligned} 8\frac{5}{6} \\ - 2\frac{2}{3} \\ \hline \end{aligned}$

**4.** $\begin{aligned} 5\frac{7}{8} \\ - 3\frac{3}{4} \\ \hline \end{aligned}$

**5.** $6.38 \times 10 =$ _____

**6.** $0.753 \div 100 =$ _____

**7.** $56.2 \times 100 =$ _____

**8.** $3.5\overline{)7.21}$

**9.** $6.2\overline{)4.34}$

**10.** $1.6\overline{)35.6}$

**11.** $2.5\overline{)62.5}$

# Using Weight and Capacity

Choose *ounce, pound,* or *ton* to measure each.

**1.** hamburger patty      **2.** chair      **3.** adult

_____      _____      _____

**4.** compact car      **5.** sweatshirt      **6.** coffee table

_____      _____      _____

Choose *fluid ounce, cup, pint, quart,* or *gallon*
to measure the capacity of each.

**7.** teacup      **8.** large saucepan      **9.** can of juice

_____      _____      _____

Complete.

**10.** 2 gal = _____ pt      **11.** 8 fl oz = _____ c      **12.** 4 lb = _____ oz

**13.** 48 oz = _____ lb      **14.** 5 gal = _____ qt      **15.** 2 lb 3 oz = _____ oz

Choose the most reasonable unit of measure for each.
Write *c, gal, oz,* or *lb.*

**16.** A big bowl holds 2 _____ of soup.      **17.** A nail weighs 2 _____.

**18.** A bat weighs 1.5 _____.      **19.** A bathtub holds 18 _____ of water.

## Review and Remember

Add, subtract, multiply, or divide.

**1.** $\begin{array}{r} 3.5138 \\ + 2.8704 \\ \hline \end{array}$      **2.** $\begin{array}{r} 2.9384 \\ + 7.8421 \\ \hline \end{array}$      **3.** $\begin{array}{r} 5.73 \\ - 2.973 \\ \hline \end{array}$      **4.** $\begin{array}{r} 3.0693 \\ - 1.25 \\ \hline \end{array}$

**5.** $\begin{array}{r} 392 \\ \times 222 \\ \hline \end{array}$      **6.** $\begin{array}{r} 837 \\ \times 161 \\ \hline \end{array}$      **7.** $232\overline{)34{,}104}$      **8.** $400\overline{)56{,}415}$

    

Name _____

# Estimating and Measuring Length

Choose the most reasonable unit of measure for each.
Write *km, m, cm,* or *mm*.

**1.** distance a car travels in 15 minutes

_____

**2.** length of a kitchen

_____

**3.** thickness of a quarter

_____

**4.** length of your hand

_____

**5.** distance around a baseball diamond

_____

**6.** distance around a city

_____

Write the missing unit. Use *km, m, cm,* or *mm*.

**7.** A pen is about 15 _____ long.

**8.** A piece of tape is less than 1 _____ thick.

**9.** A rabbit is about 30 _____ long.

**10.** Some cross-country ski races are 5 _____ long.

**11.** A diesel truck is about 16 _____ long.

**12.** A kitchen counter is about 1 _____ high.

Use mental math to complete.

**13.** 8 m = _____ km    **14.** 2 cm = _____ m    **15.** _____ cm = 58 m

**16.** 66 mm = _____ cm    **17.** 17 cm = _____ mm    **18.** _____ m = 92 km

## Review and Remember

Solve by using mental math.

**1.** $0.015 \times 100$

_____

**2.** $6.13 \div 100$

_____

**3.** $24.17 \times 1,000$

_____

**4.** $124.17 \div 1,000$

_____

**5.** $64.17 \times 10$

_____

**6.** $4.07 \div 100$

_____

**32**   Use after Grade 6, text page 283.                        © Silver Burdett Ginn Inc.

# Estimating and Measuring Mass

Choose the most reasonable unit of mass to measure each.
Write *t, kg, g,* or *mg.*

**1.** watch _____      **2.** couch _____      **3.** button _____      **4.** trailer _____

**5.** seed _____      **6.** dresser _____      **7.** ship _____      **8.** chipmunk _____

Write the missing unit. Use *t, kg, g,* or *mg.*

**9.** A burger has a mass of about 100 _____.

**10.** A person has a mass of about 35 _____.

**11.** A car has a mass of about 1.5 _____.

**12.** A raisin has a mass of about 5 _____.

Use mental math to complete.

**13.** 4 kg = _____ g          **18.** 231 mg = _____ g

**14.** _____ kg = 8 t          **19.** 8,000 g = _____ kg

**15.** _____ mg = 6.5 g          **20.** _____ g = 8,500 mg

**16.** 55 g = _____ kg          **21.** 70 t = _____ kg

**17.** 300 kg = _____ t          **22.** 5.7 kg = _____ g

## Review and Remember

Add, subtract, multiply, or divide.

**1.** $\begin{array}{r} \$2.75 \\ +\ 3.29 \\ \hline \end{array}$
**2.** $\begin{array}{r} 67.1 \\ +\ 44.9 \\ \hline \end{array}$
**3.** $\begin{array}{r} 5.4 \\ -\ 3.2 \\ \hline \end{array}$
**4.** $\begin{array}{r} 7.88 \\ -\ 2.99 \\ \hline \end{array}$
**5.** $\begin{array}{r} \$10.07 \\ -\ 5.22 \\ \hline \end{array}$

**6.** $\begin{array}{r} 7.3 \\ \times\ 2.9 \\ \hline \end{array}$
**7.** $\begin{array}{r} 4.8 \\ \times\ 5 \\ \hline \end{array}$
**8.** $\begin{array}{r} 0.86 \\ \times\ 0.03 \\ \hline \end{array}$
**9.** $9\overline{)0.468}$
**10.** $0.16\overline{)516}$

# Estimating and Measuring Capacity

Circle the letter of the most reasonable measure.

**1.** cup of cocoa

   **a.** 2.5 L

   **b.** 225 mL

   **c.** 225 L

**2.** jug of cider

   **a.** 4 L

   **b.** 4 mL

   **c.** 44 mL

**3.** baby food jar

   **a.** 10 mL

   **b.** 100 mL

   **c.** 100 L

**4.** bowl of soup

   **a.** 1.75 mL

   **b.** 17.5 mL

   **c.** 175 mL

**5.** water for a bathtub

   **a.** 85 L

   **b.** 850 L

   **c.** 8.5 L

**6.** large carton of milk

   **a.** 2.4 L

   **b.** 240 mL

   **c.** 2.4 mL

Write the missing unit. Use *kL*, *L*, or *mL*.

**7.** A hot water heater has a capacity of 400 _____.

**8.** A tablespoon holds about 15 _____.

**9.** A large fountain holds about 750 _____ of water.

**10.** A bottle of window cleaner holds 650 _____.

**11.** A large bottle of shampoo holds 1 _____.

**12.** A glass of milk contains 250 _____.

Use mental math to complete.

**13.** 6 L = _____ mL

**14.** 3,000 mL = _____ L

**15.** _____ mL = 7.2 L

**16.** 3.5 kL = _____ L

**17.** 2,000 L = _____ kL

**18.** 4,500 mL = _____ L

## Review and Remember

Estimate.

**1.** $\begin{array}{r} \$17.25 \\ + 13.92 \\ \hline \end{array}$

**2.** $\begin{array}{r} \$5.33 \\ + 2.07 \\ \hline \end{array}$

**3.** $\begin{array}{r} 25.7 \\ - 9.91 \\ \hline \end{array}$

**4.** $\begin{array}{r} \$6.52 \\ - 3.99 \\ \hline \end{array}$

**5.** $\begin{array}{r} 7.07 \\ - 6.88 \\ \hline \end{array}$

**6.** $\begin{array}{r} 0.35 \\ \times 0.02 \\ \hline \end{array}$

**7.** $\begin{array}{r} 0.019 \\ \times 0.9 \\ \hline \end{array}$

**8.** $\begin{array}{r} 3.02 \\ \times 0.9 \\ \hline \end{array}$

**9.** $3.6\overline{)0.252}$

**10.** $0.40\overline{)6.480}$

# Relating Units

Tell whether you should multiply or divide to find each answer.
Then use mental math to complete.

**1.** 3.5 kg = _____ g

_____

**2.** 8.25 km = _____ dm

_____

**3.** 900 mm = _____ dm

_____

**4.** 2,000 L = _____ kL

_____

**5.** _____ g = 689.5 mg

_____

**6.** _____ L = 17,400 mL

_____

Compare. Write >, <, or = in each ◯.

**7.** 3.6 L ◯ 350 mL

**8.** 2.8 kg ◯ 2,800 g

**9.** 8.4 g ◯ 0.84 kg

**10.** 5.7 m ◯ 0.057 km

**11.** 6.3 m ◯ 63,000 mm

**12.** 10,000 mL ◯ 10 L

**13.** 0.7 km ◯ 70 m

**14.** 2 kL ◯ 200 L

**15.** 29,000 mm ◯ 30 m

**16.** 300 mg ◯ 3 g

**17.** 4 L ◯ 400 mL

**18.** 7,000 mg ◯ 7 g

Complete by writing a decimal or whole number.

**19.** 5 km = _____ m

**20.** 20 cm = _____ m

**21.** 6 mg = _____ g

## Review and Remember

Write two related division facts for each equation.

**1.** $7 \times 4 = 28$

_____

_____

**2.** $6 \times 9 = 54$

_____

_____

**3.** $8 \times 7 = 56$

_____

_____

**4.** $3 \times 12 = 36$

_____

_____

Find the value of $n$.

**5.** $6 \times n = 36$

$n =$ _____

**6.** $45 \div n = 9$

$n =$ _____

**7.** $n \div 8 = 8$

$n =$ _____

**8.** $n \times 7 = 49$

$n =$ _____

Name _____

# Reading and Writing Ratios

Look at the drawing. Write each ratio three ways.

**1.** footballs to soccer balls _____

**2.** tennis balls to footballs _____

**3.** basketballs to soccer balls _____

**4.** footballs to round balls _____

**5.** tennis balls to all balls _____

Write three equivalent ratios for each.

**6.** 1:3               **7.** 8:3                    **8.** 3:2

_____     _____          _____

Are the ratios equivalent? Write *yes* or *no*.

**9.** $\frac{3}{4} = \frac{9}{12}$      **10.** $\frac{14}{22} = \frac{7}{11}$      **11.** $\frac{6}{8} = \frac{9}{18}$      **12.** $\frac{25}{50} = \frac{50}{100}$

_____            _____            _____            _____

**13.** $\frac{1}{3} = \frac{3}{4}$      **14.** $\frac{3}{4} = \frac{8}{3}$      **15.** $\frac{33}{99} = \frac{2}{6}$      **16.** $\frac{7}{8} = \frac{14}{16}$

_____            _____            _____            _____

# Review and Remember

Add, subtract, multiply, or divide.

**1.**　3.662
　　+ 2.791

**2.**　2.8729
　　+ 5.004

**3.**　6
　　− 4.387

**4.**　9.2879
　　− 5.3493

**5.**　314
　　× 192

**6.**　9,753
　　× 240

**7.** $32\overline{)6{,}819}$

**8.** $51\overline{)1{,}218.9}$

# Rates and Proportions

Circle the better buy.

**1.** 16 oz for $3.01
12 oz for $2.49

**2.** 4 donuts for $0.88
6 donuts for $0.99

**3.** 30 oz for $5.50
45 oz for $8.00

**4.** 3 peppers for $0.97
9 peppers for $2.97

**5.** 50 paper clips for $0.35
60 paper clips for $0.95

**6.** 2 loaves of bread for $1.59
3 loaves of bread for $2.29

Write each proportion.

**7.** 2 is to 5 as 4 is to 10 _____

**8.** 10 is to 1 as 100 is to 10 _____

**9.** 14 is to 4 as 7 is to 2 _____

**10.** 30 is to 5 as 42 is to 7 _____

Is each a proportion? Write *yes* or *no*.

**11.** $\frac{5}{4} = \frac{10}{8}$

**12.** $\frac{1}{2} = \frac{3}{4}$

**13.** $\frac{1}{3} = \frac{6}{9}$

**14.** $\frac{2}{5} = \frac{4}{10}$

_____

_____

_____

_____

**15.** $\frac{3}{10} = \frac{9}{30}$

**16.** $\frac{4}{28} = \frac{2}{7}$

**17.** $\frac{2}{3} = \frac{4}{9}$

**18.** $\frac{6}{8} = \frac{3}{2}$

_____

_____

_____

_____

# Review and Remember

Solve. Write each answer in simplest form.

**1.** $7\frac{1}{6}$
$+ 7\frac{2}{3}$
_____

**2.** $8\frac{9}{10}$
$+ 7\frac{3}{5}$
_____

**3.** $11\frac{2}{3}$
$- 6\frac{1}{2}$
_____

**4.** $6\frac{5}{8}$
$- 1\frac{3}{4}$
_____

**5.** $\frac{4}{5} \times 10 =$ ___

**6.** $\frac{3}{4} \times 16 =$ ___

**7.** $\frac{3}{4} \div \frac{1}{8} =$ ___

**8.** $\frac{4}{7} \div \frac{6}{7} =$ ___

Name _____

# Using Scale Drawings

Use a ruler and the scale to find the actual length.

**1.**

scale  1 cm : 3 m

actual
length = _____

**2.**
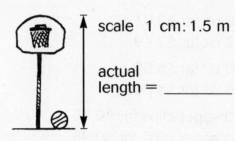
scale  1 cm : 1.5 m

actual
length = _____

The scale is 3 cm : 6 m. Use estimation to choose the actual distance.

**3.** length of the drawing:
  6.9 cm

  **a.** 9.1 m
  **b.** 13.8 m
  **c.** 36.9 m

**4.** width of the drawing:
  16.5 cm

  **a.** 33 m
  **b.** 20 m
  **c.** 33.7 m

**5.** height of the drawing:
  24.9 cm

  **a.** 16.2 m
  **b.** 39 m
  **c.** 49.8 m

Solve.

**6.** Mr. Green's new house is drawn to a
  scale of 3 cm : 4 m. In the drawing it is
  30 cm high. What is the actual height?

**7.** The tree outside Mr. Green's bedroom
  has a height of 5.6 m. If it is drawn to a
  scale of 2 cm : 2.8 m, how high would
  the drawing be?

_____    _____

## Review and Remember

Solve. Write each answer in simplest form.

**1.** $3\frac{5}{8}$
  $+ 2\frac{7}{8}$

**2.** $4\frac{2}{5}$
  $+ 9\frac{1}{5}$

**3.** $9\frac{1}{2}$
  $- 3\frac{1}{4}$

**4.** $15\frac{1}{3}$
  $- 8\frac{5}{6}$

**5.** $9 \times \frac{2}{3} =$ _____

**6.** $12 \times \frac{1}{4} =$ _____

**7.** $7 \times \frac{1}{2} =$ _____

**8.** $\frac{1}{3} \times 6 =$ _____

**9.** $\frac{3}{4} \div \frac{7}{8} =$ _____

**10.** $\frac{2}{3} \div \frac{1}{6} =$ _____

**11.** $\frac{4}{5} \div \frac{7}{8} =$ _____

**12.** $\frac{5}{6} \div \frac{2}{3} =$ _____

Name _____

## Using Probability to Make Predictions

**1.** Jennifer tossed a coin 20 times and got 7 heads and
13 tails. If tails was the favorable outcome, what is the
ratio of favorable outcomes to the number of trials? _____

**2.** If heads was the favorable outcome, what is the ratio of
favorable outcomes to the number of trials? _____

Use the lettered tiles to find each probability.

**3.** P(A) = _____        **4.** P(a vowel) = _____

**5.** P(consonant) = _____        **6.** P(M) = _____

**7.** If all the letters in the alphabet were put in a hat, what is
the probability of drawing A, E, I, O, or U? _____

You roll a 6-sided number cube and then pick one of the
lettered tiles above. Find each probability.

**8.** P(6, F) = _____        **9.** P(even number, consonant) = _____

**10.** P(prime number, vowel) = _____        **11.** P(9, consonant) = _____

**12.** P(a number less than 9, B) = _____        **13.** P(odd number, R) = _____

## Review and Remember

Add, subtract, multiply, or divide.

**1.**  2.535
    + 3.987

**2.**  6.1075
    + 4.9641

**3.**  10.987
    −  6.543

**4.**  43.9642
    − 39.4731

**5.** $1\frac{1}{2} \times 2\frac{1}{2}$        **6.** $3\frac{1}{4} \times 2\frac{1}{5}$        **7.** $12\frac{3}{20} \div 2\frac{1}{4}$        **8.** $2\frac{1}{3} \div 3\frac{1}{2}$

Use after Grade 6, text page 325.

Name _____

# Tree Diagrams

**1.** Suppose you use a spinner and a 6-sided number cube.
Draw a tree diagram to show all possible outcomes.

**2.** Sam has 2 pairs of pants (jeans and corduroys) and 3 shirts
(black, tan, and gray). List all the possible choices of outfits.

_____

_____

_____

## Review and Remember

Add, subtract, multiply, or divide. Write the fractions in simplest form.

| | | | |
|---|---|---|---|
| **1.** 0.735 <br> + 1.372 | **2.** 1.2345 <br> + 6.7890 | **3.** 9.374 <br> − 2.468 | **4.** 4.7532 <br> − 2.1980 |

**5.** $3\frac{2}{3}$ $\times \frac{7}{8}$  **6.** $2\frac{1}{4}$ $\times \frac{4}{5}$  **7.** $1\frac{1}{2}$ $\times \frac{3}{4}$  **8.** $6\frac{7}{8}$ $\times \frac{2}{5}$

**9.** $12\frac{2}{5} \div 4\frac{2}{3} =$ _____  **10.** $5\frac{5}{6} \div 1\frac{3}{4} =$ _____  **11.** $3\frac{1}{8} \div 2\frac{1}{2} =$ _____

Name _____

# Exploring Percents

Write a ratio and a percent for each shaded part.

**1.**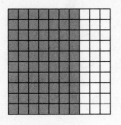

**2.**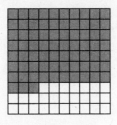

**3.**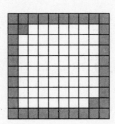

**4.**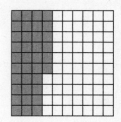

_____   _____   _____   _____

Write each percent as a ratio in simplest form.

**5.** 20% = _____   **6.** 25% = _____   **7.** 50% = _____   **8.** 19% = _____

**9.** 30% = _____   **10.** 96% = _____   **11.** 35% = _____   **12.** 37% = _____

Solve.

**13.** 64% of the students bring their own lunch to school. What percent buy lunch?

**14.** Shelly spent 89% of her allowance last month. What percent of her allowance did she save?

_____   _____

## Review and Remember

Solve. Write each answer in simplest form.

**1.** $7\frac{7}{10}$
$+ \, 3\frac{4}{5}$

**2.** $12\frac{2}{3}$
$+ \, 10\frac{4}{6}$

**3.** $13\frac{9}{10}$
$- \, \frac{1}{5}$

**4.** $25\frac{17}{24}$
$- \, 9\frac{7}{8}$

**5.** $4\frac{1}{4} \times 2\frac{14}{17}$ _____

**6.** $3\frac{1}{2} \times 2\frac{2}{3}$ _____

**7.** $2\frac{1}{4} \times 1\frac{7}{9}$ _____

**8.** $12\frac{1}{2} \div 3\frac{1}{3}$ _____

**9.** $9\frac{11}{12} \div 4\frac{1}{4}$ _____

**10.** $2\frac{6}{25} \div 1\frac{2}{5}$ _____

# Relating Ratios, Decimals, and Percents

Write each as a percent.

**1.** $\frac{3}{4}$ = _____   **2.** $\frac{3}{10}$ = _____   **3.** $\frac{3}{5}$ = _____   **4.** $\frac{16}{64}$ = _____

**5.** 0.72 = _____   **6.** 0.09 = _____   **7.** 0.56 = _____   **8.** 0.5 = _____

**9.** 0.4 = _____   **10.** $\frac{9}{20}$ = _____   **11.** $\frac{4}{5}$ = _____   **12.** 0.398 = _____

Write each as a decimal and a ratio.

**13.** 70% = _____   **14.** 87% = _____   **15.** 28% = _____

**16.** 1% = _____   **17.** 49% = _____   **18.** 12% = _____

Compare. Write >, <, or = in each ⬭ .

**19.** 15% ⬭ 0.15   **20.** 10% ⬭ $\frac{1}{10}$   **21.** 5% ⬭ 0.5

**22.** 11% ⬭ 0.1   **23.** 22% ⬭ 0.2   **24.** 75% ⬭ 0.7

**25.** 67% ⬭ $\frac{16}{25}$   **26.** 69% ⬭ $\frac{7}{10}$   **27.** 100% ⬭ 1.0

## Review and Remember

Estimate each length. Then measure to the point named.

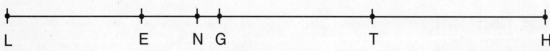

L         E     N G        T      H

**1.** from E to G

   nearest $\frac{1}{2}$ inch _____

**2.** from E to N

   nearest $\frac{1}{8}$ inch _____

**3.** from G to H

   nearest $\frac{1}{4}$ inch _____

**4.** from L to G

   nearest $\frac{1}{16}$ inch _____

**5.** from G to T

   nearest $\frac{1}{4}$ inch _____

**6.** from N to T

   nearest $\frac{1}{8}$ inch _____

# Finding Sales Tax

Estimate first. Then find the sales tax and the total cost.

**1.** cost: $3.25
   rate of sales tax: 6%

**2.** cost: $14.65
   rate of sales tax: 6.25%

**3.** cost: $36.99
   rate of sales tax: 4%

_____     _____     _____

Complete the chart.

|     | Cost | Rate of Sales Tax | Sales Tax | Total Cost |
| --- | --- | --- | --- | --- |
| **4.** | $22.00 | 4.25% | | |
| **5.** | $34.05 | 6% | | |
| **6.** | $95.00 | 8.25% | | |
| **7.** | $5.25 | 2.75% | | |
| **8.** | $29.95 | 5.5% | | |

## Review and Remember

Solve. Write each fraction in simplest form. Then
write an estimate to check your answer.

**1.** $2\frac{1}{2}$
   $+ 1\frac{2}{3}$

**2.** $6\frac{7}{12}$
   $+ 2\frac{1}{4}$

**3.** $6\frac{7}{8}$
   $- 3\frac{3}{4}$

**4.** $7$
   $- 4\frac{3}{4}$

**5.** $7$
   $\times\ 100$

**6.** $9.32$
   $\times\ 1{,}000$

**7.** $3.4\overline{)7.82}$

**8.** $0.47\overline{)9.87}$

# Computing Discounts

Find the discount.

**1.** $\$14.99 \times 25\%$

**2.** $\$25.00 \times 33\%$

**3.** $\$16.99 \times 15\%$

_____

_____

_____

**4.** $\$108.99 \times 5\%$

**5.** $\$65.95 \times 75\%$

**6.** $\$12.99 \times 33\%$

_____

_____

_____

Find the sale price.

**7.** regular price: $\$24.99$
rate of discount: 25%

**8.** regular price: $\$40.00$
rate of discount: 33%

**9.** regular price: $\$275.00$
rate of discount: 15%

_____

_____

_____

**10.** regular price: $\$99.99$
rate of discount: 50%

**11.** regular price: $\$36.99$
rate of discount: 5%

**12.** regular price: $\$34.99$
rate of discount: 30%

_____

_____

_____

## Review and Remember

Solve. Write each answer in simplest form.

**1.** $\frac{5}{9} - \frac{2}{18} = n$

**2.** $\frac{4}{5} + \frac{1}{2} = n$

**3.** $\frac{11}{20} - \frac{1}{4} = n$

$n = $ _____

$n = $ _____

$n = $ _____

**4.** $1\frac{1}{12} - \frac{2}{6} = n$

**5.** $\frac{9}{20} - \frac{3}{10} = n$

**6.** $\frac{5}{8} + \frac{4}{5} = n$

$n = $ _____

$n = $ _____

$n = $ _____

**7.** $\frac{5}{6} - \frac{2}{3} = n$

**8.** $2\frac{1}{2} + \frac{3}{5} = n$

**9.** $\frac{1}{2} - \frac{3}{8} = n$

$n = $ _____

$n = $ _____

$n = $ _____

Name _____

# Estimating and Finding the Percent of a Number

Use mental math to estimate.

**1.** 30% of 45 = _____    **2.** 48% of 60 = _____    **3.** 75% of 52 = _____

Solve. Use mental math, paper and pencil, or a calculator.

**4.** 8% of 800 = _____    **5.** 13% of 200 = _____    **6.** 31% of 300 = _____

**7.** 47% of 600 = _____    **8.** 69% of 450 = _____    **9.** 92% of 115 = _____

Find the interest. Use a calculator if you wish.

| | Principal | Rate of Interest | Time | |
|---|---|---|---|---|
| **10.** | $2,000 | 11% | 2 yr | _____ |
| **11.** | $1,200 | 13% | 5 yr | _____ |
| **12.** | $5,300 | 8% | 10 yr | _____ |
| **13.** | $420 | 9% | 1 yr | _____ |

**14.** Dave bought a car. He borrowed $4,000 at 12% for 4 years. How much interest did he pay? What was the total amount of the loan?

_____

_____

**15.** John bought a boat. He borrowed $7,500 at 15% for 1 year. How much interest did he pay? What was the total amount of the loan?

_____

_____

## Review and Remember

Solve. Write each answer in simplest form.

**1.** $\frac{3}{4}$
$+ \frac{1}{8}$
_____

**2.** $\frac{1}{6}$
$+ \frac{3}{4}$
_____

**3.** $\frac{7}{10}$
$- \frac{3}{5}$
_____

**4.** $\frac{8}{9}$
$- \frac{1}{3}$
_____

**5.** $3\frac{2}{3} \times \frac{7}{8} =$ _____    **6.** $2\frac{1}{4} \times \frac{4}{5} =$ _____    **7.** $3\frac{3}{4} \div 1\frac{1}{2} =$ _____    **8.** $2\frac{1}{4} \div 3\frac{1}{3} =$ _____

# Classifying, Measuring, and Estimating Angles

Match.

**1.** _____ an angle measuring exactly 180°          **a.** acute

**2.** _____ an angle measuring less than 90°          **b.** right

**3.** _____ an angle measuring exactly 90°          **c.** straight

**4.** _____ an angle measuring between 90° and 180°          **d.** obtuse

Use a protractor to find the measure
of each angle for the figure on the right.

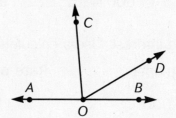

**5.** ∠ DOB _____     **6.** ∠ COD _____

**7.** ∠ AOB _____     **8.** ∠ AOD _____

Estimate the measure of each angle.

**9.**           **10.**           **11.** 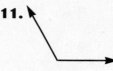          **12.**

_____          _____          _____          _____

Use a protractor to draw each angle.

**13.** 135°                    **14.** 45°                    **15.** right angle

## Review and Remember

Add or subtract.

| | | | | | | | |
|---|---|---|---|---|---|---|---|
| **1.** | 4.813<br>+ 3.73 | **2.** | 0.2915<br>+ 1.3973 | **3.** | 48.352<br>+ 30.273 | **4.** | 6.0679<br>+ 3.1497 |
| **5.** | 7.149<br>− 4.826 | **6.** | 90.015<br>− 69.842 | **7.** | 9.6312<br>− 2.9071 | **8.** | 14.06<br>− 3.073 |

# Intersecting and Parallel Lines

Write *intersecting, perpendicular,* or *parallel* for each.

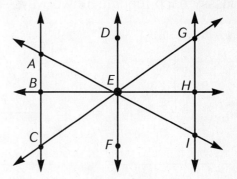

**1.** $\overleftrightarrow{DE}$ and $\overleftrightarrow{BH}$ _____

**2.** $\overleftrightarrow{AC}$ and $\overleftrightarrow{AI}$ _____

**3.** $\overleftrightarrow{AC}$ and $\overleftrightarrow{GI}$ _____

**4.** $\overleftrightarrow{EB}$ and $\overleftrightarrow{AC}$ _____

**5.** $\overleftrightarrow{CG}$ and $\overleftrightarrow{DF}$ _____

**6.** $\overleftrightarrow{AB}$ and $\overleftrightarrow{DE}$ _____

Draw a figure for each.

**7.** $\overleftrightarrow{RS} \parallel \overleftrightarrow{TU}$

**8.** $\overleftrightarrow{AB} \perp \overleftrightarrow{CD}$

**9.** $\overrightarrow{NQ} \perp \overrightarrow{MP}; \overrightarrow{OR} \parallel \overrightarrow{NQ}$

**10.** $\overline{AB} \perp \overline{BD}; \overline{BD} \perp \overline{CD}; \overline{CD} \perp \overline{AC}$

## Review and Remember

Write each in standard form.

**1.** $7^4 =$ _____     **2.** $12^2 =$ _____     **3.** $5^3 =$ _____     **4.** $10^4 =$ _____

Write each equivalent measure.

**5.** 6 km = _____ m

**6.** 14 L = _____ kL

**7.** 6.5 g = _____ mg

**8.** 34 cm = _____ m

Name _____

# Classifying Triangles

Classify each triangle in two ways—by its sides and by its angles.

**1.**

**2.**

**3.**

**4.**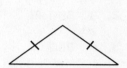

_____    _____    _____    _____

_____    _____    _____    _____

Use a ruler and a protractor to draw each triangle.

**5.** acute scalene

**6.** right isosceles

Find the measure of each missing angle.

**7.**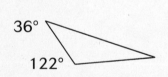

**8.**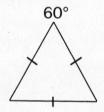

**9.**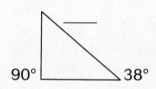

_____    _____    _____

## Review and Remember

Add, subtract, multiply, or divide.

**1.**  23.8
  + 49.6

**2.**  $76.14
  +  8.37

**3.**  $4.30
  − 3.95

**4.**  67.91
  − 35.52

**5.**  35.6
  ×  2.9

**6.**  56.78
  × 12.3

**7.**  6)15.18

**8.**  9)71.01

Name _____

# Classifying Quadrilaterals

Classify each quadrilateral two or more ways.

1.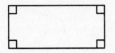

2.

3.

_____    _____    _____

_____    _____    _____

Find the measure of each unmarked angle.

4.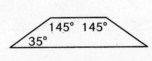

5.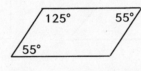

6.

_____    _____    _____

Write the letter of the polygon next to its correct description.

7. _____    a parallelogram with all sides congruent

8. _____    a rectangle with four congruent sides

9. _____    has exactly one pair of opposite sides parallel

10. _____    a parallelogram with four right angles

**a.** trapezoid

**b.** parallelogram

**c.** rhombus

**d.** rectangle

**e.** square

## Review and Remember

Use patterns to find each product.

1. $10 \times 6 =$ _____        $100 \times 6 =$ _____        $1{,}000 \times 6 =$ _____

2. $8 \times 40 =$ _____        $8 \times 400 =$ _____        $8 \times 4{,}000 =$ _____

3. $9 \times 50 =$ _____        $90 \times 50 =$ _____        $900 \times 500 =$ _____

Name _____

# Classifying Polygons

Classify each polygon.

**1.**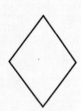

**2.**

**3.**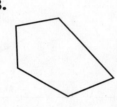

**4.**

_____  _____  _____  _____

**5.**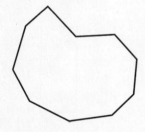

**6.**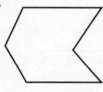

**7.**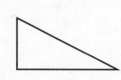

**8.**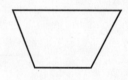

_____  _____  _____  _____

Draw all the diagonals for each figure.

**9.**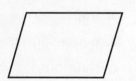

**10.**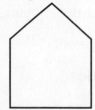

**11.**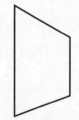

**12.**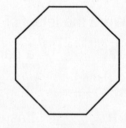

## Review and Remember

Solve. Then estimate to check. Write both the actual and estimated answers.

**1.**  4.9
    + 3.8

Estimate _____

**2.**  4.25
    + 9.45

Estimate _____

**3.**  53.27
    + 9.09

Estimate _____

**4.**  27.91
    + 18.07

Estimate _____

**5.**  5.0
    − 2.7

Estimate _____

**6.**  $20.00
    −  9.97

Estimate _____

**7.**  4.65
    − 2.86

Estimate _____

**8.**  13.18
    − 5.78

Estimate _____

Name _____

# Estimating and Finding Perimeter

Find the perimeter of each polygon.

**1.**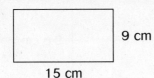

9 cm

15 cm

_____

**2.**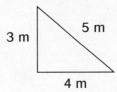

3 m   5 m

4 m

_____

**3.**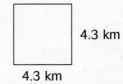

4.3 km

4.3 km

_____

**4.**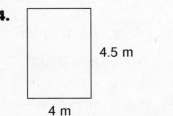

4.5 m

4 m   _____

**5.**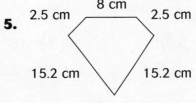

2.5 cm   8 cm   2.5 cm

15.2 cm   15.2 cm

_____

**6.**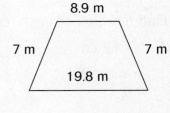

8.9 m

7 m   7 m

19.8 m

_____

Find the perimeter of each regular polygon.

**7.** triangle

$s = 12$ cm

$P =$ _____

**8.** square

$s = 4$ m

$P =$ _____

**9.** octagon

$s = 8$ mm

$P =$ _____

**10.** hexagon

$s = 15$ cm

$P =$ _____

Estimate the perimeter of each. Then measure and add to find the actual perimeter.

**11.** the top of your teacher's desk

Estimate _____ Actual _____

**12.** your notebook

Estimate _____ Actual _____

## Review and Remember

Solve. Write each fraction in simplest form.

**1.**  $3\frac{4}{5}$
      $+ 2\frac{1}{5}$

**2.**  $5\frac{1}{4}$
      $+ 7\frac{1}{2}$

**3.**  $9\frac{5}{6}$
      $+ 4\frac{1}{3}$

**4.**  $9\frac{7}{8}$
      $- 2\frac{3}{8}$

**5.**  $10\frac{3}{8}$
      $- 6\frac{3}{4}$

**6.**  $4\frac{5}{7}$
      $- 2\frac{6}{7}$

**7.** $0.52 \times 9 =$ _____

**8.** $24.3 \times 0.6 =$ _____

**9.** $8.124 \div 2 =$ _____

# Finding Area

Find the area of each figure.

**1.**

5 cm

**2.** 30 m

15 m

**3.**

9.6 cm

4 cm

_____   _____   _____

Find the area of each rectangle.

**4.** $l = 12$ cm

$w = 8$ cm

$A=$ _____

**5.** $l = 9.6$ m

$w = 2.5$ m

$A =$ _____

**6.** $l = 10$ mm

$w = 25$ mm

$A =$ _____

**7.** $l = 1.75$ km

$w = 3$ km

$A =$ _____

Find the area of each parallelogram.

**8.** $b = 20$ cm

$h = 4$ cm

$A =$ _____

**9.** $b = 12.5$ ft

$h = 6$ ft

$A =$ _____

**10.** $b = 27$ m

$h = 3$ m

$A =$ _____

**11.** $b = 2.8$ ft

$h = 6.2$ ft

$A =$ _____

## Review and Remember

Solve. Then write your estimate to check.

**1.** $\frac{3}{10} + \frac{3}{5}$

**2.** $1\frac{2}{5} + 2\frac{1}{4}$

**3.** $\frac{7}{9} - \frac{1}{3}$

**4.** $4\frac{1}{5} - 2\frac{1}{10}$

**5.** $0.12 \times 0.23$

**6.** $1.23 \times 4.2$

**7.** $15\overline{)92{,}070}$

**8.** $40\overline{)20{,}004}$

Name _____

# Finding Area of Parallelograms and Triangles

Find the area of each parallelogram and triangle in square units.

**1.**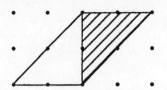

parallelogram _____

triangle _____

**2.**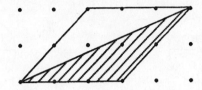

parallelogram _____

triangle _____

**3.**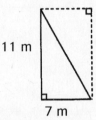

11 m

7 m

**4.**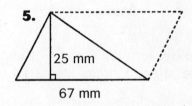

1.2 km

2.3 km

**5.**

25 mm

67 mm

parallelogram _____

parallelogram _____

parallelogram _____

triangle _____

triangle _____

triangle _____

Find the area of each triangle.

**6.** $b = 3$ cm     $A =$ _____     **7.** $b = 7.2$ m     $A =$ _____

    $h = 7$ cm                        $h = 1.9$ m

Find the area of each parallelogram.

**8.** $b = 0.7$ m     $A =$ _____     **9.** $b = 15$ mm     $A =$ _____

    $h = 1.4$ m                        $h = 7.4$ mm

## Review and Remember

Complete.

**1.** 4 L = _____ mL     **2.** _____ kg = 7.5 g     **3.** _____ mm = 49 cm

**4.** 167 m = _____ km     **5.** 0.015 kg = _____ g     **6.** 416 mg = _____ g

**7.** _____ L = 25 mL     **8.** _____ cm = 4.1 m     **9.** _____ mL = 0.47 L

Name _____

# Finding Circumference and Area of Circles

Use the formula $C = \pi d$ to find the circumference of each circle. Use 3.14 for $\pi$.

**1.**

3 cm

$C =$ _____

**2.**

1.8 m

$C =$ _____

**3.**

20 cm

$C =$ _____

**4.** $r = 3.2$ cm

$C =$ _____

**5.** $r = 4$ cm

$C =$ _____

**6.** $r = 5$ m

$C =$ _____

Use the formula $A = \pi r^2$ to find the area of each circle. Use 3.14 for $\pi$.

**7.**

2.2 cm

$A =$ _____

**8.**

4.5 cm

$A =$ _____

**9.**

7.2 m

$A =$ _____

**10.** $d = 6.7$ m

$A =$ _____

**11.** $r = 2.1$ cm

$A =$ _____

**12.** $r = 7$ cm

$A =$ _____

Find the circumference and the area of circles with these diameters.

**13.** $d = 1.3$ cm

$C =$ _____

$A =$ _____

**14.** $d = 11$ cm

$C =$ _____

$A =$ _____

**15.** $d = 0.4$ m

$C =$ _____

$A =$ _____

## Review and Remember

Multiply or divide.

**1.** $\begin{array}{r} 1.8 \\ \times\, 3.7 \\ \hline \end{array}$

**2.** $\begin{array}{r} 7.9 \\ \times\, 4.9 \\ \hline \end{array}$

**3.** $100\overline{)64.1}$

**4.** $10\overline{)32.1}$

Name _____

# Finding Volume

Find the volume of each rectangular prism.

**1.**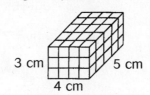
4 m
1 m
2 m

V = _____

**2.**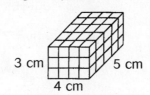
3 cm
5 cm
4 cm

V = _____

**3.**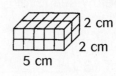
2 cm
2 cm
5 cm

V = _____

**4.**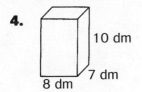
10 dm
7 dm
8 dm

V = _____

**5.**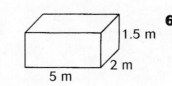
1.5 m
2 m
5 m

V = _____

**6.**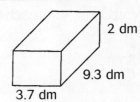
2 dm
9.3 dm
3.7 dm

V = _____

**7.** l = 5 cm
w = 3 cm
h = 5 cm

V = _____

**8.** l = 9 dm
w = 9 dm
h = 9 dm

V = _____

**9.** l = 2.6 m
w = 3.7 m
h = 4 m

V = _____

**10.** l = 12 cm
w = 9 cm
h = 8 cm

V = _____

**11.** l = 7.3 cm
w = 3 cm
h = 4 cm

V = _____

**12.** l = 6 dm
w = 4 dm
h = 2 dm

V = _____

**13.** l = 0.5 m
w = 0.3 m
h = 0.2 m

V = _____

**14.** l = 8 cm
w = 8.9 cm
h = 5 cm

V = _____

## Review and Remember

Solve.

**1.**    0.5
     + 0.6

**2.**    1.31
     − 0.94

**3.**  $17.00
     − 14.39

**4.**    7.83
     + 1.45

**5.** 0.3 + 0.45 _____

**6.** $3.92 + $5.73 _____

**7.** 0.97 − 0.29 _____

**8.** 6.25 − 4.9 _____

**9.**    3,256
     ×      7

**10.**    1,796
      ×      38

**11.**  4)$9,625

**12.**  12)3,807

# Reading, Writing, and Comparing Integers

Write an integer for each phrase.

**1.** 800 feet below sea level _____

**2.** 3 degrees below zero _____

**3.** positive 17 _____

**4.** negative 7 _____

**5.** a deposit of $30 _____

**6.** a withdrawal of $49 _____

**7.** the opposite of ⁺65 _____

**8.** the opposite of ⁻1 _____

Compare. Write > or < in each ◯ .

**9.** ⁺6 ◯ ⁻11

**10.** ⁻7 ◯ ⁺5

**11.** ⁺4 ◯ ⁺8

**12.** ⁻4 ◯ ⁺4

**13.** ⁺11 ◯ ⁻8

**14.** ⁻7 ◯ ⁻9

Use the number line. Write the integers in order from least to greatest.

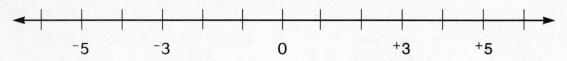

⁻5      ⁻3      0      ⁺3      ⁺5

**15.** 0 ⁻6 ⁻1 _____

**16.** ⁺3 ⁻3 ⁻2 _____

**17.** ⁺5 ⁻3 ⁺2 _____

**18.** ⁻4 ⁻6 ⁺3 _____

## Review and Remember

Choose the best estimate.

**1.** 33% of 200

  **a.** 33

  **b.** 66

  **c.** 128

**2.** 40% of 92

  **a.** 4

  **b.** 9

  **c.** 36

**3.** 22% of 81

  **a.** 1

  **b.** 16

  **c.** 22

**4.** 78% of 52

  **a.** 7

  **b.** 40

  **c.** 78

Estimate the area.

**5.**

$3\frac{1}{5}$ in.

  **a.** 7 in.²

  **b.** 9 in.²

  **c.** 12 in.²

**6.**

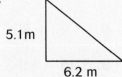

5.1 m

6.2 m

  **a.** 15 m²

  **b.** 25 m²

  **c.** 36 m²

**7.**

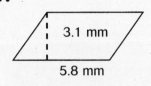

3.1 mm

5.8 mm

  **a.** 6 mm²

  **b.** 9 mm²

  **c.** 18 mm²

**8.**

5 ft

  **a.** 4 ft²

  **b.** 16 ft²

  **c.** 75 ft²

# Adding Integers

In the charts, match the black checkers with the white
checkers to find the number of unpaired checkers.
Write a number sentence to represent each picture.

**1.**

| + Black | − White | Unpaired |
|---------|---------|----------|
| ● | ○ | |
| ● | | |
| ● | | |
| ● | | |
| ● | | |
| + | = | |

**2.**

| + Black | − White | Unpaired |
|---------|---------|----------|
| ● | ○ | |
| ● | ○ | |
| ● | ○ | |
| ● | ○ | |
| | ○ | |
| + | = | |

Add. Use a number line if you wish.

**3.** $^+6 + {}^-3 =$ _____

**4.** $^-7 + {}^+2 =$ _____

**5.** $^+8 + {}^-5 =$ _____

**6.** $^+3 + {}^+4 =$ _____

**7.** $^+3 + {}^-7 =$ _____

**8.** $^-1 + {}^+2 =$ _____

**9.** $^-5 + {}^-3 =$ _____

**10.** $^+5 + {}^-5 =$ _____

**11.** $^-6 + {}^+2 =$ _____

**12.** $^+7 + {}^-11 =$ _____

**13.** $^-4 + {}^-9 =$ _____

**14.** $^-5 + {}^-4 =$ _____

## Review and Remember

Solve. Write each fraction in simplest form.

**1.** $\frac{2}{5}$ $+ \frac{1}{5}$

**2.** $\frac{1}{7}$ $+ \frac{5}{14}$

**3.** $\frac{1}{6}$ $+ \frac{1}{2}$

**4.** $\frac{5}{9}$ $- \frac{2}{9}$

**5.** $\frac{11}{15}$ $- \frac{2}{5}$

**6.** $\frac{4}{7}$ $- \frac{1}{7}$

**7.** $4.8$ $\times 2.7$

**8.** $4.37$ $\times 5.2$

**9.** $14\overline{)5.04}$

**10.** $52\overline{)69.68}$

Name _____

## Subtracting Integers

Fill in the blanks and the chart to illustrate $^+1 - {^-4}$.

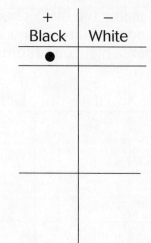

| + | – |
|---|---|
| Black | White |
| ● | |

1. Start with _____ black checker.

2. Add _____ white checkers.

   Add _____ black checkers.

   $^+4 + {^-4} =$ _____

3. Take away _____ white checkers.

   The result is _____.

Subtract.

**4.** $^+7 - {^-5} =$ _____   **5.** $^+5 - {^-6} =$ _____   **6.** $^+4 - {^-2} =$ _____

**7.** $^+14 - {^-15} =$ _____   **8.** $^-6 - {^+4} =$ _____   **9.** $^-9 - {^+10} =$ _____

**10.** $^-1 - {^-6} =$ _____   **11.** $^+12 - {^+12} =$ _____   **12.** $^-5 - {^+4} =$ _____

**13.** Monday the temperature was $^-3°C$. Tuesday the temperature was $^-6°C$. How many degrees less is $^-6°C$ than $^-3°C$?

**14.** The tip of an iceberg sits 10 ft above sea level. The iceberg reaches a depth of 80 ft. How tall is the iceberg?

_____   _____

## Review and Remember

Solve.

**1.**  123
      + 45

**2.**  4,568
      + 168

**3.**  16,872
      − 9,642

**4.**  25,875
      − 16,999

**5.**   45
      × 82

**6.**  172
      × 92

**7.** 89$\overline{)4,984}$

**8.** 12$\overline{)6,744}$

Name _____

# Locating and Graphing Ordered Pairs

Write the ordered pair for each point.

**1.** A _____    **2.** B _____

**3.** C _____    **4.** D _____

**5.** E _____    **6.** F _____

**7.** G _____    **8.** H _____

**9.** I _____    **10.** J _____

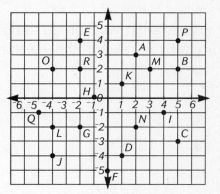

Name the point for each ordered pair.

**11.** (−4, +2) _____    **12.** (+3, +2) _____    **13.** (−4, −2) _____    **14.** (+5, +4) _____

**15.** (−5, −1) _____    **16.** (+2, −2) _____    **17.** (+1, +1) _____    **18.** (−2, +2) _____

Graph each point. Connect the points in order.
Name each figure formed.

**19.** (−1, +1), (+1, +1), (+1, −1), (−1, −1) _____

**20.** (0, +3), (+2, −2), (−2, −2) _____

**21.** (−4, +2), (+4, +2), (+4, −2), (−4, −2) _____

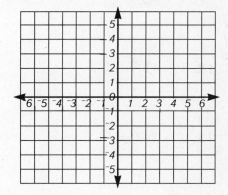

## Review and Remember

**1.** Sue has 5 pairs of socks, 3 pairs of jeans, and 7 T-shirts.
How many outfits does Sue have?

_____

**2.** Bill is making snacks to take hiking. He has 4 types of dried fruits
and 3 types of nuts. How many different snacks containing
1 type of fruit and 1 type of nut can he make?

_____

# Operations and Solving Addition and Subtraction Equations

Explain what you can do to both sides of each equation to find the value of the variable. Then solve.

**1.** $z - 3 = 5.1$

_____

**2.** $t + 1.6 = 8$

_____

**3.** $r - 18 = 100$

_____

**4.** $s + 11 = 76$

_____

**5.** $d - 5.6 = 8$

_____

**6.** $n + 18 = 100$

_____

Solve each equation. Then check your solution.

**7.** $x + 42 = 62$

_____

**8.** $r - 6 = 36$

_____

**9.** $p + 14 = 32$

_____

**10.** $j + 41 = 113$

_____

**11.** $m - 72 = 25$

_____

**12.** $a - 29 = 46$

_____

**13.** $x + 5.7 = 15.6$

_____

**14.** $q + 35 = 61$

_____

**15.** $m - 15.5 = 15.2$

_____

Find the value of the variable for each equation. Write the related fact you used.

**16.** $r + 78 = 130$

$r =$ _____

_____

**17.** $v + 24 = 57$

$v =$ _____

_____

**18.** $m - 67 = 28$

$m =$ _____

_____

## Review and Remember

Solve.

**1.**  275
    $+ 303$

**2.**  456
    $- 327$

**3.**  2,653
    $+ 1,245$

**4.**  762
    $\times\ 3$

**5.**  589
    $\times\ 8$